How much stock should one place phrase, *research shows...*

Research shows that the prescription pain-reliever, Vioxx, is a safer alternative to aspirin, yet Vioxx was withdrawn from the market in September of 2004 after leading to at least 88,000 heart attacks and strokes, and after contributing to the deaths of an estimated 38,000 individuals.

Research shows SSRI anti-depressants like Paxil and Zoloft are safe and effective treatments for depression, yet there have been an alarming number of suicides connected with the drugs, one of many known side-effects that have been repeatedly downplayed by drug manufacturers.

And now, "new and exciting" research shows that a freshly patented anti-anxiety medication similar to Klonopin holds promise for treating autistic behaviors even though a key benzodiazepine researcher, more than thirty years ago, called for follow-up studies to confirm or rule out suspected brain damage for millions who had suffered after taking the drugs. Those studies have yet to be undertaken.

The science-as-sales-tactic, *research shows,* delivered a bill of goods to returning college student and single parent, Laurie Oakley. One she never bargained for. Anti-depressants prescribed by her general practitioner were the gateway drugs that landed her squarely into the mental health system where she continued to experience the side-effects of multiple medications; these side-effects were repeatedly misdiagnosed as a worsening mental illness. After even her medical doctors labeled her a hypochondriac while overlooking the side-effects of medications clearly listed in her chart, she decided to do some research of her own. She recovered her health, save for persistent insomnia that sent her back for more treatments. This time, when presented with medication treatments that she knew could cause harm, she would insist upon accountability. While her story may not manage a happy ending, she nevertheless closes on an unexpected high note.

CRAZY

AND IT WAS

Surviving the
Corporate Pharmaceutical Corruption
of
Western Medicine

LAURIE OAKLEY

Indie River Press
Cincinnati

CRAZY AND IT WAS

Copyright © 2015 by Laurie Oakley

ISBN: 0990855147
ISBN 13: 978-0-9908551-4-9

Cover Illustration by Suzanne Mills
Author Photograph by Francine Ris

Printed in the United States of America

Some names and identifying details have
been changed to protect the privacy of individuals.

This book is not intended as a substitute for the medical advice of a physician.
Before making any healthcare or treatment decisions you should
consult with a qualified professional.

Publisher's Cataloging-in-Publication data:

Oakley, Laurie.
Crazy and it was : surviving the corporate pharmaceutical corruption of western
medicine / Laurie Oakley.
p. cm.
ISBN 978-0-9908551-4-9
Includes bibliographical references.

1. Oakley, Laurie. 2. Mental illness --Biography. 3. Mental Disorders--drug therapy--
Personal Narratives. 4. Drugs --Marketing. 5. Pharmaceutical industry --United
States. 6. Medicine --United States. I. Title.

RC464 .O35 2014
616.89 --dc23   2014952527

For Kenton—

Survivor extraordinaire

CONTENTS

PART TWO: THE CONFLICT

PART THREE: THE GRIEVANCES

PART FOUR: THE RESPONSES

PREFACE

I need to begin this book by telling some things that it is not. This is not a book against the use of all medication. It is my personal belief that most medication, in the right hands and with the right knowledge, is useful. Neither is this a book intended to encourage anyone to stop taking any medication. To the contrary, stopping a prescription medication can be as life-altering as taking one and is only advisable with the help and support of a knowledgeable physician. Lastly, this book has not been written with the aim of swaying anyone toward believing any particular opinion. I am obviously not an expert in medicine or psychiatry, nor do I have any credentials, (thanks in no small part to what is laid out in this book).*

What this book is is my story, told in a well-researched context. I have woven my personal narratives together with old journal entries, medical records, and several researched sections. When deciding which journal entries and medical records to use, I chose those which best showed what I was experiencing at the time, those mentioning the medications I was taking, the symptoms and side-effects I presented with as well as the impact these were having on my life, and how the professionals from whom I sought care responded.

I have edited my journals and minimally edited the medical records to make a more coherent story. Nothing has been significantly altered or fabricated. Names of persons and institutions have been changed, and mention of minor health concerns have been removed, as well as unrelated personal and family details. If for some readers it appears that something is missing from my records, please note that these are primarily medication monitoring records transcribed in the same format in which I received them. I did not include records such as assessments or therapy notes as the focus of this book is the use and misuse of pharmaceuticals. My intention is to present a true and readable story, not forensic evidence.

While the views of those whose work I cite in my researched sections have not gone unchallenged by people in high places within psychiatry and academia, nevertheless I am grateful to them for speaking out and revealing what they know in regard to the pharmaceutical industry's utter dominance of today's healthcare systems. What they reveal is in accordance with my experience, and that validation has been central to my being able to understand and tell what happened to me.

Many who question the validity of my sources indignantly remind us that there are millions who are helped by pharmaceuticals and that for anyone to attempt to put the brakes on the way medicines are promoted within today's healthcare system is to deny people who are suffering much needed relief. This needs to be seen for what it is: smokescreen. It is not enough that pharmaceutical manufacturers reach those for whom their drugs work in order to make their living. It is when they reach those for whom the drugs do not work so well that these companies make a killing. This book depicts how medication side-effects are chronically missed, misdiagnosed, and treated with more pharmaceuticals, making people like me patients for life.

*Some readers may take exception to my use of words such as *paradoxical* and *cognitive* as if I am trying to write with authority despite my lack of credentials. I would kindly ask that it be kept in mind that scholarly books and articles are the tools I used to dig my way out of the pharmacological avalanche. Consequently, my vocabulary in this writing is reflective of that study.

CRAZY
AND IT WAS

"How did these beautiful rainbow-tints
get into the shell of the fresh-water clam,
buried in the mud at the bottom of our dark river?"

— *Henry David Thoreau*

PROLOGUE

Grace and Marley,   *July 7, 2007*

    Early this morning while you slept, I slipped out of the house and made my way to Emergency Services at UC Hospital. I saw a doctor after two hours of waiting, got two prescriptions for sleep, and a doctor's note for a day off of work. I felt relieved that I was half way home before one of you called. It was you Marley, at 9:15 a.m., wanting a ride to the car wash for the high school band. I was glad, this time, my condition did not have to affect my parenting.

    You have watched me for over two and a half years now, trying not to have a condition. You watched me in withdrawal from Klonopin after I swore off services altogether. You got yourselves off to school every morning while I slept if I could, and I usually could, after being up four and five hours in the night. You have finished my sentences with understanding when my tired brain could not come up with the right words. You listen with patience as I caution you against relying upon substances, prescribed or not. I have served as the best and worst example of why you shouldn't use alcohol, experiment with drugs, or put too much trust in your doctor's prescribing powers. A sensitive system, an intricate biology, and susceptibility to stress are said to be passed along in the DNA. If that is the case, your dad and I have given you magnificent yet disturbable DNA.

    This morning I caved. I gave up my attempt to function without medication. I recognized that in order to take another step, I would need to get some help.

PART ONE

THE TELLING

"The public must decide whether it
wishes to continue on the present road, and it
can do so only when in full possession
of the facts."

*— Rachel Carson, American writer, scientist,
and ecologist who warned against the
indiscriminate use of chemicals.*

1

Emergency Room

July 2007

I WALKED INTO THE emergency room at the University of Cincinnati Medical Center a little after 5:30 a.m., exhausted. I'd had trouble sleeping since I quit taking the prescription drug Klonpin (clonazepam) almost three years earlier. It was the last on a long list of medications I had been prescribed for depression by my primary care physicians and community mental health practitioners in Kansas over a period of eight years. Not only could I not get off of it without experiencing horrible insomnia, it caused other problems while I was taking it: memory loss, mental confusion, and tolerance withdrawal symptoms that were repeatedly misdiagnosed as psychosomatic complaints during the last four years I had taken it.

Once I had figured this out, I tapered myself off of Klonpin and endured a horrible withdrawal. By night, sleep was replaced with hours of my laboriously trying to mentally outfox panic attacks. By day, I functioned half-dazed with throbbing head and aching body and a tsunami of adrenaline surging in my gut. Over time, the withdrawal symptoms lessened, and I remained hopeful that the ability to sleep I'd had before starting the medications would return. In attempting to improve my life, I moved to a new city while taking on more and more responsibility: I entered a significant relationship, started working full-time, took on house and car payments, on top of raising my two children. Their father had died of a sudden heart attack when they were seven and nine and now they were fourteen and sixteen. By May of 2007, I had called the Community Mental Health Access Point who had taken my insurance information saying they would verify my benefits and call back. After receiving no call, I had little energy to pursue it further.

This seemed to be the defining characteristic of my condition: a massive energy crisis from which I felt powerless to take another step. Although I dropped to part-time employment, giving up some of my responsibilities as a personal care assistant, I still couldn't function well at any of my jobs. I guess I'd had it. After nearly three years of attempting to function in spite of extreme sleep deprivation, something inside of me decided to call it quits. This part of me knew better than to act on fantasies I'd had in the week prior to this emergency room visit. I would not be jumping from a bridge into the Ohio river, nor would I be stuffing my Tuesday lady into the trunk of the car and forgetting about her. I had responsibilities and kids to think about, and I was actually very fond of my Tuesday lady.

Medication was on a list of things I expected to get from this visit. From past experience, I had a pretty good knowledge of what to expect from anti-depressant, anti-psychotic, and anti-anxiety drugs. I came to the emergency room, for one, to ask for a small dose of Seroquel (quetiapine fumarate). I knew from taking it years earlier that it would help me sleep without causing the problems that drugs like Klonopin had. Secondly, I wanted a doctor's note. I had accrued sick leave for over a year but had no way of accessing it without a doctor's note. But the most surprising of my three wishes was for reentry into the system. For nearly three years I had struggled to remain free from services, trying every alternative treatment over getting in line for more drugs. Yet none of these could undo the insomnia that medications had precipitated in my brain. This was the last place I wanted to be, yet in order to function I had to return to the healthcare system.

For my first request I didn't even need to ask. My story opened up an entire psycho-pharmaceutical medicine cabinet, the doctor suggesting a whole host of medications. Lamicial, Topamax, and Depakote were used as mood stabilizers, as were Neurontin and Lithium. Cymbalta, Effexor, and Wellbutrin were in another class of anti-depressants, any of which could be mine for the taking. All I had to do was choose one and then work out the details with the doctor she would refer me to. My report of anti-depressant induced panic attacks and suicidal depression didn't slow down her pitch. Before she was finished she had given me an entire lesson on brain function and chemistry, left and right hemisphere, for free. I expressed concern of how medications might affect the heart arrhythmia I had developed but had never had checked out. Cardiac arrhythmias ran in my family, and while I'd been mostly fine with having only a relatively few uncomfortable episodes over the course of many years, they were becoming more frequent and it concerned me as I was approaching middle age. She assured me the medicines she was talking about would be safe. Having known me ten minutes she told me exactly how certain medications would straighten out my particular brain. Until that could be worked out she would prescribe the Seroquel I wanted and an antihistamine called Hydroxyzine for anxiety.

My second request proved much more difficult. I had been dragging myself to work day after day despite this chronic sleep debt. I hoped at the emergency room I could get a note to use my sick leave for some much needed time off to rest. But when I mentioned this, the doctor's generous, drug pushing momentum slowed to a more cautious, authoritarian approach.

I walked out of the Emergency room with a note for one day off work and the two prescriptions. After nearly three years of struggling alone, I was back in the system. The system I tried to abandon, the system that had abandoned me. More an outrage than a story, I might not believe it if I had not been so unfortunate to live it.

Journal Entry

June, 1996

The divorce is final, the kids' school is out. I'm sitting here at the beginning of summer deciding how to move forward. I need to make a plan and take action.

I'm depressed of course. So is it any wonder things aren't going well? With the kids I'm depressed, but it's not them. They are foremost on my mind. I need to find the energy to take care of us, and our home. No matter how much I sleep, I have no energy. Sometimes I wish I didn't have to wake up and face the day.

I'm in school and that is okay. I can be both a good mother and a student. Most of the time when I'm with the kids I'm "somewhere else," especially with all of the junk that's been going on. Nothing is more important than the quality time I spend with them. They need a predictable routine.

We've had the new dog for a couple of weeks and they seem to really enjoy her. Grace is so gentle with her. She named her Joy and that's what she brings.

What kinds of things can I do to make our time together more meaningful? Perhaps the end of the day can be "our time." Maybe I can have a small surprise for them at the end of the day, or something special they can look forward to. We can make a good dinner together. Since I don't see them all day, mostly I want to be there and listen. I need to get down on their level and pay more attention.

I will make an appointment to see the doctor. Maybe he can prescribe something.

SSRI ANTIDEPRESSANTS

In 1996, antidepressants like Prozac and Paxil were making the news. The American public was being told these drugs corrected a deficiency in the brain of a certain chemical called serotonin. We were told these newer drugs were better than the older tricyclic antidepressant medications. They had been developed specifically to enhance the chemical serotonin without causing the side-effects that were common with the older medications.

I was receptive to this. At 31, recently divorced and a mother of two preschoolers, I was taking classes at a local university while also working part-time. Most days I felt I was in over my head and felt too stressed to cope. At school I overheard conversations in my social work classes by students who were taking antidepressants, SSRIs they were called. Many of them said they were taking Paxil and that it really helped them to deal with stress.

The chemical imbalance aspect made sense to me because as someone who had struggled with mood swings and a consistent, low-grade depression for most of my life, I had suddenly felt better during my first pregnancy. For many years I had spent hours in therapy to address my past and personal issues and yet none of this seemed to matter as soon as I was pregnant. After the birth of my daughter, even though I maintained the healthy diet and self-care practices I had established during pregnancy, the depression gradually returned.

Imagine watching Disney's movie, *The Parent Trap,* as an eight-year-old, rooting for the twin sisters who met at summer camp and conspired to get their divorced parents back together. Imagine being ambushed during the movie's happy ending by a hopeless grief because you knew that in real life kids don't have that kind of power; your parents would remain split and you would be required to live out your childhood with the step-mother who hated you. Now imagine the doom of that moment following you throughout your life. That is what

7

chronic, low-grade depression felt like for me, and shaking it off would have been as impossible as putting my parents' fractured marriage back together.

Despite my time in therapy, I experienced this continual heaviness. I could get through my days but thought surely people were supposed to feel better than this. Prominent doctors were now saying that research showed the key to unlocking depression was largely chemical and there were medications to help. That fit my experience. I was all in.

2

Cornerstone

Mike/August 2007

NOT LONG AFTER MY emergency room visit, I became a client at Cornerstone Health. Cornerstone is one of the many federally licensed community mental health agencies in America that provide services to individuals who have mental health and/or substance abuse issues. Agency staff assist clients to develop comprehensive and individualized treatment plans to further their recovery from many different conditions including depression, anxiety, and substance abuse.

My new therapist, Mike, was a tall, Tom Hanks like character. He was down to earth, treated me as an equal, and was easy to work with. In order to see the psychiatrist, I needed to meet regularly with Mike. He apologized as he faced the computer to take some notes. It was agency protocol, and aggravating, he said. He asked me how to spell the word *definite* as he sat typing, trying to sound it out. This was much different from my former therapist in Kansas who over the years had sat facing me with pen and paper in hand. I didn't mind. I had no desire to be back in the system except to receive Seroquel for sleep.

I was not unaware that Seroquel could cause metabolic disorders. I also knew there could be even more serious side-effects. While at that time Seroquel did not yet have a heart warning, I was aware that any fairly new drug could have side-effects that hadn't yet been identified.

Since I had taken Seroquel in the past and had fewer problems than with so many other psychotropic medicines, I decided that its sedating effects would be worth it in light of the extreme exhaustion my chronic insomnia caused. For me, this was a quality of life issue. By this point, Seroquel was the lesser of two evils.

Along with taking Seroquel, I began to make lifestyle changes to reduce my workload and stress. I transitioned out of the two jobs that made up my full-time employment and started a part-time position that paid better as an independent provider supporting individuals with disabilities. The downside of this was that I lost healthcare coverage for myself and my family. I began commuting to work by bicycle to both save money on gas and to get exercise that might help me sleep. I continued sleep hygiene practices I had begun in the two years prior, things like getting to bed at the same time each night, avoiding tv, computer, and cellular phone screens in the hours before bed, and avoiding caffeine and sugar.

I tried different herbal remedies, melatonin supplements, and essential oils. While some of these helped temporarily, none worked for long. Whenever I mentioned insomnia, most people suggested I drink chamomile tea. Of course I had tried it, but I got tired of telling people this so I pretended to be interested.

At my appointments, Mike and I talked about the things I was doing to reduce stress and improve my chances of getting a good night's sleep. I also brought up my history and the anger I felt about what had happened to me. I told him about having reactions to medications that doctors did not even recognize as side-effects.

Mike responded by saying, "Don't I know it!" and told me about two family members who were being treated for chronic medical conditions and who were also inundated with medication prescriptions and side-effects. While he didn't discount anything I related about my experience, what he did say was this: "We do things differently here."

Journal Entry

August 1, 1996

Where has the summer gone? I feel so off balance! So many times I decide how I will take care of us and later can't even remember planning it.

Is this too much change or the anti-depressants? I feel out of touch and tired all the time. I just need to level out. Five different anti-depressants have not helped. I have felt so bad.

The doctor gave me a medicine called Klonopin which helps me tolerate the anti-depressants a little better but I'm not taking care of the kids the way I wanted. I've been so nasty toward them. Today was a bad day, especially because I have no energy.

Marley was so precious in his red striped tank top play-ing on the patio and picking up roly-poly bugs. Silly boy asked if I wanted to "pet"one but all I wanted was to go in-side. Grace was riding in circles on the Big Wheel in the driveway while talking to Catherine on the cordless phone. I wish I was able to enjoy them more.

Maybe Grace starting Kindergarten will bring some re-lief? Hopefully starting my social work courses in the fall will help.

My moods aren't stable. Usually it's hard to remember yesterday let alone last week or month. And I just can't bring myself to exercise. Now Dr. Terrell wants to try lithi-um. Since the anti-depressants caused panic attacks, he thinks I may have bi-polar depression.

All I know is that I'm at a loss for concrete direction and

I'm tired of dealing with my own junk all the time. How can I make the best of this? Most of all, what about the kids?

CHEMICAL SOLUTIONS

In 1996, well-known neuroscientist and former director of the National Institute of Mental Health, Stephen Hyman, wrote a paper describing how psychiatric drugs disrupt brain functioning. In his research he found that the brain makes compensatory adaptions in response to the chemicals and that these adaptations are actually maladaptations compared to normal brain functioning. While there is no evidence to support the claim that biochemical imbalances in the brain are what cause mental illness, drug manufacturers like Eli Lilly and GlaxoSmithKline promote drugs such as Prozac and Paxil as medications to correct such imbalances.

According to Irving Kirsch, an expert in clinical trial methodology and author of the book, *The Emperor's New Drugs*, in the case of the first SSRI anti-depressant medication, Prozac, the early drug tests were so unconvincing that numerous tests had to be thrown out before the company finally got the three successful studies they would need to win FDA approval. The drug barely had any effect over a placebo in most subjects. One effect, however, seen with Prozac and not the placebo, was patient suicide. In the early 1990's, The *British Medical Journal* (BMJ) received Eli Lilly documents from an anonymous source that revealed the company had observed, during clinical trials, many other problematic side effects: agitation, mania, and psychosis in people who had not experienced these things before taking the drug. From the very first trial people were recognizing that Prozac was a dangerous drug. Nearly 40 percent of participants dropped out of clinical trials because of side-effects. The manufacturer's response was to cover this up. Some results were thrown out in favor of more positive findings, others were simply re-coded. For example, if a patient experienced a psychotic episode, the researcher might put down a worsening of depression instead. Prozac was approved by the FDA and launched onto the market in 1987.

Prozac was just one of several SSRIs I was given. When taking it resulted in nightmares and panic attacks, my doctor moved on to the

13

next one. I wouldn't even begin to tell which drug caused what as I was given so many in quick succession. All I know is that I was seeking relief from depression and ended up having a major upheaval in my brain. This was something I could ill afford. Having been raised in a turbulent home, I was predisposed to being highly sensitive to stress as well as to having chronic depression. I had grown up fetching my dad's Pabst Blue Ribbon beers, cheerfully delivering them to him on the couch so I could solve the word puzzles printed on the underside of the caps. What I was never able to figure out was why the eggshells under my feet always gave way, leaving me a target of his deep-seated rage and my step-mother's cool, calculated hatred. Predictably, I left that home only to find myself in a troubled marriage. A couple of dry drunks, this time. A modest improvement perhaps, but I wasn't willing to settle. After five years of trying to address the violence that only escalated with each passing year, I decided to call it quits. When I finally got out of the marriage, I felt my kids and I deserved a shot at a good life. I had no idea that seeking help from my doctor could lead toward, and not away from, chaos.

One of the biggest problems I had after being put on these drugs was that my mental processes became so clouded that I had no way of making sense of what was happening to me. I had lost my closest social connections in my church during my divorce and also lacked a strong connection to family. I had no support system. I believed in the idea that I was receiving a professional treatment backed by science, and so was willing to proceed with those treatments despite the uncomfortable side-effects I was told would be temporary.

3

Cornerstone

Dr. McDonnell/September 2007

I MET WITH CORNERSTONE psychiatrist, Dr. McDonnell, shortly after my appointment with Mike. She was classy, like Candice Bergen, peering over the top of her bi-focals. Sitting on the other side of her desk from me, she reclined in her chair with her arms folded. I told her things had been going better for me on Seroquel. I took a small amount before bed which for the most part helped me to sleep. Both my partner Nick and I noticed I was not as mentally together while on it. I began having trouble recalling the details of even recent events, and sometimes lost my way while navigating familiar routes within the city. I also noticed a feeling of heaviness I didn't like, but while these things were disturbing, they were a price I was willing to pay to at least get some sleep.

With Dr. McDonnell, I dove right in with my story of former treatments that had caused major disruptions in my life. Like Mike, she had a "you don't have to tell me" take on the subject. She seemed to recognize problems related to taking benzodiazepines like Klonopin long-term, and told me how she never, ever prescribed the stuff. As a psychiatrist, she viewed clients seeking benzodiazepines as the primary problem.

The benzodiazepine class of drugs were chemical compounds that had been discovered in the early 1960's. They immediately began calming the waters for both patients and doctors, but became controversial when it was later acknowledged they could easily lead to dependency for more than a few patients. Most doctors still viewed these medicines as effective, relatively safe, and a simple solution for many of their patients.

When I told Dr. McDonnell insomnia had never been an issue for me until I got off of all medications, and that I still refused to take Klonopin even though staying off of it was difficult because of insomnia, she said she wished I could talk to the people who are always coming to her for benzodiazepines. It was as if she had a well-worn rut in which the wheels of her thinking got stuck in the idea that individuals suffering from physiological dependence to their prescribed medications were to blame for that dependence and could simply quit if they wanted to.

I guess at the time I was just relieved she believed me. My seeking Seroquel was similar to the behavior of those seeking benzodiazepines, although it wasn't a controlled substance like Klonopin. People did find ways to abuse it, though I was obviously not that far gone. Despite her casual response to my story, I felt mostly positive toward Dr. McDonnell. This would change a few years later, however, when I became aware of what she wrote in my record.

Journal Entry

November 13, 1996

I have been struggling. It seems that I can't keep track of myself. I have a hard time remembering my schedule, what day it is, etc. On top of that, I have very little energy. What can I do to get off of this treadmill?

I am getting good grades but school is demanding. I cannot escape that. Finances are stressful. And just the pressures of day to day living and the kids—it's overwhelming.

I know whatever is wrong is with me, not the kids. Even at the tender ages of three and five, they are such good friends to each other. They spend whole afternoons in their room playing pretend and laughing. A "good mom" would gather her energy and go join them. As it is, I am starting to feel my self-esteem drop, drop, drop.

I hope Dr. Terrell is right and this new medication will start to balance things out. I still have Klonopin to help with panic attacks. I need to become comfortable with my life once again.

ADVERSE EFFECTS

At the time, I was too ashamed to admit that my goal quickly changed from wanting to feel better to simply wanting to feel as I had before getting started on medications. Years earlier when I told a relative I was getting mental health services, I was warned to never let them give me medications. That was before SSRIs had been developed so he couldn't have been talking about these newer drugs that were backed by science. No matter. I was paying dearly for not heeding that advice. My depression had been a serious concern but not life threatening and didn't come close to the serious mental illness brought on by medications.

Dr. Peter Breggin, author of the book, *Medication Madness*, found that his patients had a hard time describing the feelings they experienced while taking antidepressants. "There is no adequate vocabulary to communicate the bizarre internal experience," he reported. Many physicians fail to recognize what is happening to their patients on antidepressants and often attribute problems to the patient's original condition. Some doctors believe the symptoms are an "unmasking" of underlying mental illness and in turn prescribe more drugs.

In my case, this was exactly what I was told. When I reported to my primary care physician that the medication gave me nightmares and panic attacks, always around 3 a.m., he told me point blank that SSRI medications don't cause panic attacks and that we were discovering an underlying condition. Instead of reporting these side-effects, this was when he gave me the additional drug, Klonopin, to take at night.

Though my doctors never reported my adverse effects, the reporting system, Medwatch, received more complaints about Prozac in the first two years after it hit the market than had been reported with the leading tricyclic antidepressant in 20 years. There were 39,000 reports of adverse effects from Prozac within the first 10 years. Because not all adverse effects are reported, it is estimated that the 39,000 number is only a very small percentage of the actual number of complaints.

Then came the other SSRI's like Paxil and Zoloft. The FDA's Medwatch list was filling up with complaints about these drugs while the pharmaceutical industry continued to promote them as safe. The complaints ranged from nervousness to suicidal impulses and included worsened depression, anxiety, memory loss, impotence, mania, psychosis, and hallucinations. Yet the focus was kept on those for whom the drugs did work. There were, of course, people who did well on the new SSRI's.

While those in the medical profession and the public were made aware of the success stories in regard to these new drugs, the FDA kept a lid on the steady flow of adverse effects being reported in association with these medications. Very reluctantly did they begin to acknowledge, a full decade after those reports began flowing in, that there were problems. Instead of carefully safeguarding the public as the agency was intended to do, the FDA acted as a cover for the pharmaceutical industry. And there is a good reason for this. The FDA had, by then, become funded in large part by the pharmaceutical industry.

Funding for the FDA had historically always come from taxes paid into the U.S. Treasury. In 1992, the Prescription Drug User Fee Act was passed by Congress and required pharmaceutical companies to pay a user fee to the FDA for getting their drugs reviewed and approved. The purpose was to speed up the approval process so that people who needed access to medications could receive them in a more timely manner. The passage of the user fee act meant a large share of the agency's funding would now come from the drug industry. While the pharmaceutical companies like the idea of their drugs moving through the pipeline faster, they don't necessarily like footing the bill, and they expect a return for their investment after paying those fees to the FDA. Where the American public was once seen as the client, the different arrangement in funding has meant FDA officials tend to see the pharmaceutical industry as their client. While drug safety is a stated objective of the FDA, drug company pressure all too often takes precedence.

4

Cornerstone

Vanessa/January 2009

I TOOK A BREAK FROM mental health services in 2008. My only unmanageable symptom had been insomnia and while it hadn't completely abated, I was coping well. Seroquel didn't really work after a few months of using it every day, and increased doses made me feel unwell. I put my hope in alternative approaches like herbs, meditation, 12–step work, and exercise. While my sleep wasn't great, I still enjoyed working, riding my bike, and spending time in my garden as well as with my family. I had also become part of a writers community. I continued to hope that as I focused on wellness my condition would change.

By early 2009, however, I was struggling again. I was fortunate to be a part of a caring team of personal care assistants who accommodated my situation by taking my morning shifts and letting me work in the afternoons and evenings. Since I awoke between 2 a.m. and 4 a.m. most mornings, getting back to sleep was more possible if I knew I didn't have to rise early. This way, I avoided getting back to sleep around five-thirty only to have to get up a half-hour later. Aside from the changes to my work schedule, I decided to seek help from the agency again.

When I returned to Cornerstone, Mike was not available. This didn't really bother me. He had been helpful but hadn't provided what I would consider therapy. I respected and almost preferred that, but when I began seeing a new therapist, Vanessa, I recognized right away that she would provide a more professional level of support. While my primary motivation was to have access to the medication, in regard to therapy with Vanessa, I had lucked out.

Vanessa was a fresh practitioner, sharp, and maybe a perfectionist. She sat facing me, leaning forward slightly with back erect, jotting things down. She listened with an open mind and took my report seriously. Instead of brushing aside my claim of being harmed, she held my story. She didn't blame it on the individual practitioners involved or make excuses for the system in which she worked. Though it didn't seem there was anything she personally could do, she didn't forget that it was important to me and didn't require me to move on to other topics.

At a chemical dependency training she attended, she asked the presenter if a person could have a long-term protracted withdrawal involving chronic insomnia lasting years after stopping daily use of Klonopin. At my following appointment she told me his response was not a tentative maybe but an absolute yes. Instead of denying or minimizing my pain, she had taken an interest and put forth the effort to validate what I had told her. Then she took the time to gather and provide me with information on things like nutritional supplements and sleep hygiene, and even led me through guided imagery. Eventually, we would focus on the topic of my difficult childhood.

. . . .

I was a clueless child. Pulled by the courts from my unfit mother just prior to my fifth birthday, I quickly became the pariah at my dad's after he and my stepmother were awarded custody. My first shenanigan was breaking my stepmother's arm when she fell while teaching me to roller skate. At least that was the family line. I was impulsive, put my clothes on backwards and wrong side out, and failed to comprehend the rules of social behavior at preschool. While my classmates did the Hokey Pokey and turned themselves around, I lay on the floor in the attached bathroom having a time out. For me it was a calling out, "telephone...telephone...?"

"Telephone..." a little boy answered. It worked. I got a classmate's attention. It was all fun and games until the teacher told on me.

I had no idea what my stepmother was talking about. She called it a harangue, something I was doing to her. "Why are you bad," she repeatedly asked me.

"I don't know," I repeatedly answered. This answer got me a red hand print on the cheek. It would be gone before I ended my harangue.

"You don't know—that's your stock answer! Now answer my question...why do you work so hard at being bad?" I searched every corner of my brain. Nothing.

She told me it was easy for children to be good and it took a lot of effort to be bad like me. She went on and on explaining it. Maybe for five minutes, probably thirty. It was a lot of words so I quit listening for content and focused on the *sssss* sound when she enunciated. It wasssss all gibberissssssh assss ssssshe ssssspoke on and on about sssssstuff I wasssssn't paying any attention to until the inflection in her voice rosssssse at the end of a ssssssentence and I realisssssed ssssshe wasssss assssssking me a quesssssstion. The door of her trap was slamming shut quickly so I blurted out "I don't know," which would have been true even if I had been paying attention.

Why was I bad? Why did I do it? My brain refused to help us unlock the mystery. "Answer me!" she yelled, then paused before tapping her foot. "I'm waiting...." Like a cat toying with a small cricket it never intends to eat, she reveled in my buffoonery, ceaselessly asking questions to which I had no answers. I truly didn't have any well-thought-out reasons for doing the things I did. I was five!

So for my sixth birthday, in the spirit of behavior modification, I was given a new name: Stinkpot. I remember lugging around a pan of vinegar water and a box of rags for scrubbing the woodwork as she explained to my grandmother why I wasn't to receive any presents. I'm sure I scrubbed some of it, especially when she was looking, but when given tasks like this I spent as much time as I could doing what I did best: loitering. I sat next to the coffee table where the magazines were and thumbed through the pages of toys in the Sears catalog, only touching the rag to the baseboard if I heard her coming.

I began to spend a lot of time alone at this age. Since the four other kids were older and in school and I had half-day kindergarten in the afternoons, I spent the mornings avoiding her whenever I could. I went down to the sand pile and hurled rocks at toads, watching their gooey brains ooze out until I was overwhelmed by a new feeling, guilt, and resolved never to do that again. I spent time lingering in the garage sampling dog food and sticking my doll's plastic head in my dad's vice just to see what would happen. When I couldn't avoid her, my step-mother shared little nuggets of information such as where I got the purple mark on my back side. Nerve damage from my mother's spank-ings, she said. *Really*, I thought. I wouldn't know what a birthmark was. She also let me in on how many children my dad had actually wanted: fewer than my mom ended up having with him. The wheels spun in his youngest child's head. Early on, she'd let my brothers and I in on something pretty significant, "your dad and I have to feed you, clothe you, and put a roof over your head, but that's all we have to do. We don't have to love you." Not that she ever withheld her attention, whether we needed it or not.

By the time I was seven or eight, other family members' be-longings started ending up in my room. My stepbrother Max's stacks of quarters, my stepsister Heidi's transistor radio, some red licorice missing from somebody's shoebox. When asked how it all got there, I said, "I don't know," and in a way it was true. I remembered seeing it and I remembered wanting it. That was all I remembered. I was jarred from my oblivion by my stepmother's hand in my hair; she kept it just long enough to give it a couple of good yanks, short enough for the Duckwall's store clerk to mistake me for a boy. "Little boy! Where's your mother?" she asked before evicting my older brother and me when I had stolen a Kit Kat. My "mother" was across the street at Gage Bowl with her good friend Mrs. Godfrey, clobbering the pins for a change. I hated her.

It wasn't long before I devised a plot. While loitering with the Endust and a rag in my parents' room, I opened the drawer beside the bed and found a package of lemon drops. Also in the drawer was some sort of chemical cream or medicine. I imagined putting some of that poison on the lemon drops. Maybe she would die. I imagined it when I was riding the bus; I imagined it when I was at school. I imagined it when I was sent to my room; I imagined it while loitering at the dinner table past eight o' clock, refusing to eat the salad I'd loaded with blue cheese dressing (because my favorite color was blue). The question was not whether or not she would die, but whether or not I would get away with it. Eventually, I decided not to. I was too afraid. It wasn't until I was old enough to know what contraceptive foam was that I could quit feeling afraid for what I had almost done.

In spite of being rescued from my mother's influence at the impressionable age of four, I just couldn't stop fucking it up. My stepmother said all the things good parents are supposed to say, like, "quit feeling sorry for yourself," and "get out of my sight," and "by golly, I'll give you something to cry about," yet at the end of the day, I would be dragged through the house by my hair.

. . . .

Vanessa listened to the accounts from my childhood and helped me not to discount the effects they still had on my life. She supported me as I worked through some challenging life situations, and respected my decision when I needed a break from therapy.

By the end of that year I did need a break. I might not have taken one had I known just how difficult it would be to get back in a year later. By the time I did, Vanessa was leaving, and because I lacked health insurance, I was not able to resume services with her at the clinic she moved to.

Journal Entry

March 19, 1997

Social anxiety is ruining my life. I am not so concerned with past failures as I am future contacts. Even the simplest situations cause me distress. I'm having trouble remembering people's names and even phone numbers I should know. I feel so normal and intelligent in the privacy of my own mind and I am still making good grades in school. I love learning and still want to apply myself toward earning my social work degree.

I feel tired—tired of struggling. I think this tiredness is depression. On lithium I was doing better but then started forgetting things. At first I thought it was the Buspar, but I quit taking it and still have problems. I was writing a check at the grocery store and could not even remember the year. I froze as the cashier watched and waited. It was embarrassing! I bought a book at Barnes and Noble and started to read it. Still, I forget that I even have it until I see it lying there, and then I don't even remember where I left off.

The most disturbing thing was when Susan came to pick up her daughter. She was holding a check and instead of waiting for her to hand it to me, I walked over and grabbed it. I immediately realized what I had done but was too shocked to say anything. I called later explaining it must be the medication. Thankfully, she understood. Now I am not taking any of these meds, except for Klonopin some nights, and yet this stuff keeps happening.

I go about my daily tasks not enjoying anything. I keep waiting for something to change. I really want to provide consistency for the kids, but something in me is lacking. I wonder how this affects them?

Village Behavioral Health

Oakley, Laurie A.
Progress Notes
April 22, 1997
Hour 8:30
Length 60
Goals/Objectives: Evaluation

Narrative Summary: Client is a young woman who presents with a blunted affect and complains of "panic attacks." The panic attacks occur only at night and she wakes up with them and fears that at some point her fear will cause her to lose touch with reality. She further describes discomfort in social situations. Client was difficult to follow and when I double checked what she had said, it wasn't what she intended to say. She went to her family practitioner and was put on medication. She has tried numerous anti-depressants and reports they cause panic attacks. Reports lithium was helpful, but she then developed confusion and behavior that was erratic. She has no medical problems. At times client's thoughts were not quite clear. She describes periods of confusion, and besides schizoid traits, she also demonstrated some paranoid traits. Client takes Klonopin 0.5 mg as needed for panic attacks. Discussed with client and her therapist possibility of starting her on a small dose of anti-psychotic at night. She was extremely worried about side-effects and I assured here there probably wouldn't be any.

5

Cornerstone

Dr. Elliot/February 2009

I STARTED SEEING DR. ELLIOT in February of 2009 for medication management after Dr. McDonnell had moved on. He was old school and I liked that. Sitting across from me in plain office attire and clunky, black shoes, he scribbled unintelligibly while asking the questions a psychiatrist is supposed to ask: have you had thoughts of hurting yourself, and have you had thoughts of hurting anyone else? I thought it should be obvious so I would roll my eyes and tell him, "No, of course not."

The questions went on and on. Do you have racing thoughts? Sometimes. Do you have mood swings. Doesn't everybody? Do you have temper outbursts? Only when provoked. Do you have any fun? I try.

I didn't hide the ill feelings I had toward the system from him and Dr. Elliot did try to understand. He showed genuine concern for the difficulty I experienced because of insomnia, but did not have a lot to offer in the way of treatment. He respected that given my history I didn't want to take risks with most medications; he also respected it when I did my own research. He did give me a prescription for Trazodone which I agreed to try, and when the first dose made me feel unwell, he respected my right to discontinue. He continued to prescribe the small dose of Seroquel that worked better than nothing.

Because I had given up my full-time job, I lacked health insurance. He repeatedly expressed concern over this, and always gave me drug samples. He stated several times that if it weren't for my lack of insurance, he would recommend a sleep study. I told him of how I had sold the three family house I was unable to refinance because of the faltering economy, and had even given up my car as I figured the less I owned and the fewer bills I had, the less I would need to work while severely sleep deprived. My situation had gotten me down for sure, but I told him there was also a minimalist aspect to giving up all those things that I liked. He no doubt thought this was odd, but I never got the sense that he viewed me as any kind of freak.

Some of the things Dr. Elliot asked about were subjects I was reluctant to elaborate on. I'd had questions of my own about whether my insomnia might be linked to certain kinds of abuse, but I didn't feel comfortable discussing it in the occasional thirty minute check-in sessions I had with him.

. . . .

As a child, I couldn't bear to sit on anyone's lap. My grandma would arrive and park herself on the couch and say, "come see me!" I loved it when she said that. She reached out and I climbed up and then sat unmoving, like a brick. I was afraid I would hurt her. I couldn't wait to get down.

The only lap I had been comfortable in was my mom's. We had a routine: I managed to do something bad and predictably, she slapped me. Then I ended up getting held and soothed in the warmth of her lap, enveloped in two great, soft pillows. Thrust into the new environment at my dad and stepmom's, the learning curve sent me reeling, repeatedly. I had the naughty part down, as well as the predictable smack in the face, but when it came time for the soothe, I was put my empty room to "think about it." Outside my window, lonesome tumbleweeds wandered across the scorching Kansas prairie while I sat thinking, mostly about my mom.

Dad would say "come see me," and I did, my muscles tense like hard clay. He said, "let's take a nap," and I would lie stiff like Lot's wife, a pillar of salt under his arm. Unable to dissolve, I just lay there beneath his arm until it became heavy and his nose hairs made that whistling sound. If I had an itch, I lived with it. I lay there plotting my escape, agonizing far too long before crawling out carefully as not to wake the sleeping giant.

He began showing up at my bedside in the mornings when I was about eight or nine. I awoke to him stroking my hair or my face, but usually I pretended to sleep. I hated it, but couldn't figure out why I hated it as nice as he was. I lay motionless, waiting for him to leave. One morning I "woke up" because he was picking out puzzle pieces he'd found stuck in my hair. "What is this?" he asked. I'd carefully taped together a puzzle picture of two kittens in a basket of yarn and had hung it on the wall above my headboard. Apparently, it had come unstuck from the wall while I slept. The mystery of the puzzle pieces was a welcome distraction from his loathsome advances and when it had been solved, we laughed.

These sexually motivated bedside visits were his version of quality time. But when we were out with my brother checking fishing lines along the banks of the creek and I worried aloud that I'd left my toy iron plugged in, his caring disappeared faster than a cold can of Coors, "Ah, well, Laurie..." he thought for a moment before finishing, "that's too god dammed bad!" He pulled up and baited another line. I prayed to God not to let there be a fire. *Please, God. No fire.* I sat in the rowboat for at least another forty-five minutes, imagining the flames that were engulfing our house. As my brother calmly rowed, the oars rhythmically gliding through the water and dripping upon their return, I was developing an anxiety disorder. Finally, we got out and dragged the boat onto the bank, leaving it upside down, tied to a cottonwood. *Please, please, God. No fire.* I prayed, sitting in the back of the pickup with a couple of bass and a channel cat as my dad drove slowly up the gravel road, not even leaving a trail of dust. I looked at the sky over the tree line. At least there was no smoke. As he drove past the cattle gate, I strained to see up past the ponds where the horses were grazing. At least the house was still there. He finally pulled the truck into the driveway and parked. I hopped out and ran inside, down the hallway to my room and there it was, sitting just how I'd left it. *Thank God! No fire.* I unplugged the warm iron.

He would sometimes ask questions like, "Laurie, what grade are you in now?" or "how old are you?" and I would need to give him

31

an update. While these insignificant details often escaped him, I could count on his full attention when I was lying in my bed. He also initiated this bonding while I stood at the stove making his Folgers instant coffee. He would hover from behind and put his arms around my waist like I'd seen him do with my stepmom. It had made her uncomfortable, too. I squirmed and said, "no," and "don't," while she called in from the dining room, "Laurie, don't say that. Your dad is only trying to show you love." *Great*. Janie's got a gun and all I've got is someone more clueless than I am encouraging this repulsive libertine. I was confused by how badly I hated "love," which was about as badly as I hated her. Love, after all, was the ultimate experience and everyone wanted Love. I hated his "love" but I didn't hate it as much as I hated myself for hating Love.

There was only one middle of the night visit that I remember, something I told my mom about the next time I saw her. She said she would take care of it, and she did. He denied he had done anything and was reasonable, not the least bit angry at being accused. After she talked to him he didn't do that again. Years later, she would tell me he had shown up on her doorstep to get from her what he couldn't get at home. This was right after he had annihilated her in court and had taken us kids away from her. She told him, "don't whip a dead horse," and sent him on his way. *Huh*. I liked that. I would use that one someday.

, , , ,

When I took a break from mental health services in 2010, I was able to receive medication through a clinic for low-income individuals. I was still working part-time assisting an individual with a disability, raising two teenagers, and living with my partner who also had a disability, but I felt I was doing okay. I kept looking for ways to reduce stress, but by this time the habit of forging on in spite of insomnia was well set. Most of the time I simply tried to pretend I could function like everybody else seemed to be functioning.

But by 2012, the bottom was falling out. I found myself in need of medical tests, yet when I applied for financial assistance at the hospital, I was denied. Both of my kids were in college and still living at home, as well as Grace's newest addition, Robin. Everyone I supported at home and at work had insurance coverage of some sort, but I was falling through the cracks.

I took a long hard look at my choices and realized that not only was it self-destructive to ignore my own exhaustion while focusing on others' needs, it wasn't really doing them any favors, either. I was not bringing my best self to anything I did. I made a decision to cut back again on caregiving and to begin to truly focus on my needs.

At this point, my tone with Dr. Elliot took on more urgency. I became impatient with his questions. I was tired of doing the same thing and expecting different results. There was nothing new in the way of treatments, I still had no way of paying for a sleep study, and when I suggested I might file for disability to get access to medical care he told me, "you look too good." He said I wasn't like those people who qualify for disability, that I even seemed like someone who might work in the agency.

It wasn't lost on me that I looked too good precisely because I'd refused excessive medication and worked hard to become well and to recover in spite of what meds had done to me. I knew full well how treatment with medications could tear me down to the point I would certainly look the part for a disability claim. I wasn't willing to do that to myself again.

So I began to take Dr. Elliot to task for his part in the system that had taken no responsibility for the outcome of treatments I had received. He laughed and said other clients had also said he represented "the system" and he didn't really know what that meant. I told him that if I had done to myself with alcohol what they had done to me with Klonopin, it would be well accepted that my insomnia was due to long-term chemical dependency. He replied that he could neither confirm nor deny Klonopin had hurt me, that there was no way of knowing for sure. He said if I thought something needed to be reported about how medications affected me, I should have reported it back then, to those who prescribed them.

That ended the helpful relationship I'd had with Dr. Elliot. Had I known at the time I received those medications that there would be long-term consequences, I could have reported it. It didn't become evident to me until years later and I was reporting it to *him*. In the very least, I thought, he could assist me in some effort to notify *somebody*. As it stood, I existed alone in a forlorn purgatory. While he made a good living in a system that continually denied responsibility for the outcome of its actions, I continually lived with that horrible outcome.

Journal Entry

September 9, 1997

Dull ache, compulsive overeating, ensuing frustration—I just want to die. Is this from the darkness of my childhood, or because of the divorce, or maybe the stress of single parenting and school? Is it all of it? Tonight I was so frustrated with the kids. They were nearly impossible. Why is this happening?

Really I'm not feeling well at all. If it weren't for the kids I would probably commit suicide, but I figure that is just transferring my pain onto someone else. I do not feel connected with others. Somehow I've lost my place and I don't know how to find my way back.

I am in so much pain. All I can identify is that it is mental stress due to my whole living situation. I'm not sure why it's not working out but I am sure that it is not working out.

I wish I had gotten that job with the Kansas Children's Service League. I wanted to be productive, earn some income, and possibly pull myself up out of this. I thought it would take off some of this pressure. I had been so excited about taking social work classes. Now in the middle of it, though I am making good grades, I'm doubting myself and my situation.

I took the kids to Gage Park on Saturday and they at least had some fun. They enjoyed the pony rides and also got to ride both the train and the carousel. At least I feel good that I was there with them.

SUICIDE

It wasn't until 2004 that the FDA issued a Public Health Advisory concerning risks associated with the newer antidepressant medications like Prozac and Paxil. In a public hearing, family members of people who had been prescribed these medications told of how their loved ones committed violent acts or suicide while under the influence of these drugs. In March of that year, the FDA issued the public health advisory, only acknowledging that drug-induced suicide was possible in a small percentage of children and adults.

An additional warning about side effects caused by these drugs was less publicized that included anxiety, agitation, panic attacks, insomnia, irritability, hostility, impulsivity, severe restlessness, hypomania, and mania. Dr. Peter Breggin, medical expert in criminal, malpractice, and product liability suits involving these medications stated, "From agitation and hostility to impulsivity and mania, the FDA's litany of antidepressant-induced behaviors is identical to those induced by PCP, methamphetamine, and cocaine, drugs known to cause aggression and violence. These older stimulants and most of the newer antidepressants cause similar effects as a result of their influencing brain levels of the same neurotransmitter, serotonin."

As these side effects are widely misdiagnosed as a patient's own mental illness, doctors often increase a person's dose or add more psychiatric medication. Dominique Slater was a teenage girl in California who was put on several antidepressants in 2003, including Wellbutrin and Celexa. When she did not improve and her behavior became more erratic, she was prescribed a double dose of the antidepressant, Effexor. She killed herself 15 days later.

In addition to suicide, there has been an increase in extreme and senseless violent acts in correlation with the rise of the use of these medications. GlaxoSmithKline was ordered in 2001 to pay $6.4 million to the family of 60-year-old Donald Schnell who killed his wife, daughter, and granddaughter just hours after he had begun taking Paxil.

And antidepressants aren't the only culprits. As far back as the 1980's problems with the longer-term use of benzodiazepines were recognized. These included emotional clouding, depression, psychomotor as well as cognitive and memory impairment, interactions with other drugs, and sometimes paradoxical excitement and aggressiveness. *The Handbook of Psychiatric Drug Therapy, Second Edition, 1991* states that, "All benzodiazepines have been associated with the emergence or worsening of depression; whether they were causative or only failed to prevent the depression is unknown. When depression occurs during the course of benzodiazepine treatment, it is prudent to discontinue the benzodiazepine."

A group of anti-seizure medications now used to treat mood disorders including Neurontin, Lamictal, Topamax and Depakote, have also received an FDA warning about possible side-effects such as anxiety, agitation, hostility, mania, and hypomania, many said to be precursors to emerging suicidality. Still, most physicians underestimate the risk involved while writing these prescriptions. The frequency and severity of adverse effects from antidepressants, stimulants, and tranquilizers, including suicide, is astonishingly underreported to and by the FDA and pharmaceutical industry.

37

6

Cornerstone

Peggy/March 2012

WHEN I RETURNED TO the system in 2012, my former therapist, Vanessa, was leaving so I was assigned to a woman named Peggy. I was severely stressed by a combination of things: chronic insomnia, job stress and ongoing burnout, multiple responsibilities at home, and other emerging health issues. I had a well-worn habit of neglecting my own needs and this was a first step toward changing that.

Peggy, at first, seemed like a good fit. She was older than me and I hoped she could offer some wisdom from her own life experience. But when I expressed that I had emerging health issues with no access to healthcare, things got strange.

She related a lengthy story about a time in her life when she almost died. One afternoon she developed certain symptoms. She wanted to ignore them but her husband insisted they go to the hospital. While there she took a turn for the worse but eventually recovered. She was very grateful for her husband's love and support. She was sure things would work out for me as well.

Coming back to my situation without health insurance, I told her I was falling through the cracks and hoped I might access healthcare by filing for disability. She assured me I would not be able to maintain my standard of living if I were to do that. As with Dr. Elliot, I looked a certain way to her. I must have looked like I worked full-time and owned a decent house, made car payments and went shopping or to the movies on weekends. In reality, I was struggling to work three days a week, and those were six hour shifts. I had no savings left and by this time didn't even own a house or car. None of this changed the way I looked. I didn't know about Peggy's views, but I was mindful of the cultural assumption that if someone desires disability benefits, they simply don't want to work. We wouldn't get to it, but work was the one thing in my life I had learned to get right. I enjoyed working because employers were some of the only people who hadn't told me I was a piece of crap. As long as I did good work, they appreciated me. I could never get enough.

. . . .

My first job was like one of those gigs advertised on Craigslist that promises handsome pay for exciting work but ends up landing you on the street selling knives for nothing. I was around six, and the chore list was posted on the fridge. My duties included but were not limited to: cleaning my room (making sure all dirty clothes ended up in the hamper), feeding and watering the chickens both in the morning and evening, and the same for the dogs. My starting salary was ten cents per week, paid on Saturdays. While that might not seem like a lot by today's standards, back then it would get me either a cold bottle of Fanta strawberry pop, two fistfuls of Easy Bubble bubble gum, or one delicious fistful of Tootsie Roll Pops. Unfortunately, because of a downturn in the economy due to ongoing behavioral issues, my employer was forced to make cutbacks. I was only docked two cents per offense, but it quickly added up. Oddly, the workload would increase steadily over the years, as would the salary, yet my income rarely budged from zero.

Because of an unrewarding and increasingly hostile workplace environment, loitering became my sole occupation. Dusting the furniture meant sitting at the coffee table looking at magazines. Weeding the garden meant sitting in a pile of weeds waiting for the sun to go down. Washing the dishes meant hanging out in the kitchen reading the Bigelow tea boxes and eating Domino sugar cubes. You'd think I would just do my work and get on with my day, but I'd get a hair pulling or a talking to either way, so why bother? If there were no parents nearby, I got back to the business of the simple pleasures of playing. Our black Labrador Retriever, Toby, was an ally with whom I could easily waste an hour. If we weren't playing tug of war with a rag or a rope, I might just lay beside her and watch her tail lazily smack the floor whenever I spoke to her. Often, while still on the clock, (because I was always on the clock), I was also on the swing set in the back yard, pumping so high it would tip. The hours passed while I dug in the sand with my next older brother, Patrick, pushing Tonka trucks and plastic cars through the sand pile thoroughfares he had built. Patrick was good and got his work done early. A sensitive child, he would do almost anything to avoid a harangue and even offered to do my chores if I agreed to play what he wanted to play. I took full advantage. He did my work and afterward I broke the treaty faster than he could say Andrew Jackson. We played what I wanted to play. I was a bona fide stinkpot.

I'd honed my skills when it came to the oblivion that allowed me to steal these fragments of childhood unhindered until my stepmom's mean-looking, green Ford LTD came barreling down the Two Mile Road throwing gravel and chased by a tornado of dust. Then it was back to reality. I stood at the sink dutifully washing the dishes when she came into the house and started letting me have it. It's not that I disagreed at all with her assessment that I was a despicable human being, undeserving and unlovable, it's just that I couldn't resist going out to play.

From the sixth grade on, I learned I could actually work even if I didn't want to. There would be no loitering in the hayfield. I started haying with my brothers around then and usually drove the trucks while they loaded them. But like a line of penguins diving from the frozen sea ice, my brothers each left home shortly after turning eighteen. After each departure, more work was expected from those left behind. Soon, I found myself either lugging the densely packed bales of fresh alfalfa and clover to the large trucks with hooks, or laboriously hefting them into the best stacks I could, which were nothing like Patrick's. I got to do it all over again upon reaching the barn, (also known as the sweat box). Like an ox, I was worked in the morning before it was too hot, and again in the late afternoon and into the evening, sometimes well after dark. I could rest only in the hottest part of the day, when it rained, or when lucky enough for my Dad's baler to break down. At sixteen, not only was I not sure how I'd ended up with this illustrious career, I somehow developed the crazy notion that at least some of my time and energy was my own. I began to resent having nothing left for doing what I wanted to be doing: practicing basketball. This kid was becoming a real pain in the ass.

First my dad said that farm work made us kids responsible. By god, we had a reputation in the community. Then he reminded me that my labor was for my own room and board. Well, I *had* been given the tiny room for the hired hand that had been built onto the back of the farmhouse in the earlier part of the century, (my stepmom explained I was put out there to get me "as far away from the family as possible"), but in my cluelessness I had thought the *hired* part meant the man had been getting a paycheck. Finally, my dad played his trump card, "Don't worry, Laurie, when they plant me you'll get your fair share." I liked that. I would use that one someday.

Despite all the advantages, I decided to forgo the great deal I was getting on room and board. When I was seventeen, I ran away to live at my mom's. She was a mom and I was a teenage girl and we got along like two feral cats dropped into a bucket. I lived there until the end of my senior year and then moved out, taking over the task of screwing up my own life.

My first "real" job was working part-time in a camera shop. I was somewhat of a dependable employee. Most days I arrived on time, although on one occasion I showed up waterlogged after riding to work in the rain on my little, red Honda motorcycle. *That's funny.* You get soaked in a quick minute when traveling by bike. They sent me back home for dry clothes. It took even less time for me to learn that being chained to enterprise wasn't all it had been cracked up to be. The newness wore off quickly and I dreaded going in. Calling off work wasn't as simple as skipping school. Skipping school had been easy: I just didn't go. With work I had to both pick up the phone, and lie. In this context, I wasn't comfortable doing either. I also wanted to keep the job. Ultimately, what kept me walking through those doors every day was the actual paycheck. As it turns out, money motivates. Who knew!

I quit that job when I got the opportunity to work full-time as a nanny for a year, and afterward, pieced together a living by cleaning houses and providing childcare for various individuals. Then, when I was twenty-two, I applied for work in drywall construction, a job that came with benefits. They hired me because I was tall. Right away, my two other female coworkers set me up on the extra-tall stilts, put a sanding block in my hand and pointed at the ceiling saying, "Get that." I got so tired of looking up.

The guys liked it that we were there, and not for the reasons one might think. Sanding was entry-level and nobody wanted to do it. By noon, you looked like you'd lost a fight with a sack of flour, and there would be twice that much dust in your lungs. It got in your eyes, got stuck in your nose, and you ended up drinking it in your coffee. The guys hated sanding. They were glad to have us. I was given the opportunity to learn finishing or hanging, but ended up focusing on being a mother, and later, went back to school, returning to sanding when I needed to. There were those who disapproved of a female working in this male-dominated profession, but I figured since I'd been expected to work like a man on the farm for nothing, I sure the hell had a right to do this job and get paid for it.

My dad had always wanted me to become a nurse or a secretary. I knew he thought their job was to look good for the men around them. I thought that was bullshit. The closest I ever came was working as a temp in the unemployment office for a few months in 2002, around the time he was in the final throes of cancer. *Huh.* There was a disease that could gobble up this creature who had ripped me from my mother so he could sexually objectify, mistreat, and use me for free labor. In mid-September when they planted him, I was told there was nothing to inherit, just a farm, which only made sense to leave to the boys.

. . . .

Eventually, Peggy inquired about my primary relationship. I confided some insecurity and expressed my need to explore those issues with her. While I didn't expect we would do that right then and there, I also didn't expect her to abruptly shift onto an entirely new subject: her credentials for working with me.

One of us was impressed, but it wasn't me. After asking another very personal question, she responded by telling me all about agency policies. The focus flipped awkwardly from me to her agenda for the rest of the session. Then it was time to go.

"Don't run into that trash can," she told me as I walked out the door.

Journal Entry

November 8, 1997

I don't know what has gotten me this far. I'm still struggling with intolerable feelings. I had a suicide plan on Wednesday. I fear if I did that I would have to watch the kids suffer from a distance. I wouldn't want to put them through it so I go on living like this.

Drywall work helps and I am on Remron, a new anti-depressant. Still, I feel like I'm barely hanging on. This depression I find myself in slowly crept into my being and it is essential that I find a path out from it.

I feel totally depleted and depressed. I am tired beyond belief. I don't feel like I have anything to look forward to. Every day I get up and do what is prescribed. There seems to be no freedom for me. How can I get out from under this heavy load?

Village Behavioral Health

Oakley, Laurie A.
Progress Notes
December 3, 1997
Hour: 2:30
Length: 15
Goal Progress: Fair – Good

Narrative Summary: Client reports her mood is a little better than during the last visit. She still has times when she withdraws and has little energy. Sleeping well. Decreased suicidal ideation. Remron increased to 30 mg daily. Client stopped Zyprexa and notices no difference and wants to try not taking it. She continues taking Klonopin.

7

Cornerstone

Beth/April 2012

MY RENEWED SELF-RESPECT directed me to ask for a different therapist. I was determined to make things work with Beth because I didn't want to earn a reputation for being difficult. I was eager to get to work making life changes that might ease the stress that contributed to the sleeplessness and the severe discomfort that resulted from it.

The first thing I noticed about Beth was that she did not like to make eye contact. This didn't really bother me because I'm the same way. She also had a burned out quality to her. She habitually started appointments late and ended them 10 to 15 minutes early; once I had to confront her because she was nodding off during my therapy session. She apologized, and for the most part I liked her. She had a short, no nonsense approach to working with me and was also a good listener. I had a lot to say and it helped to say it to her. Most of all, she wasn't Peggy.

By this time I had decided to bring up disability only if the positive life changes I was making failed to improve my situation. I wanted to prove that I was sincere and that filing for disability was, in fact, a last resort. I was tired but I could do this.

I told Beth about measures I was taking to change my diet to include only whole foods while cutting out processed food-like products, sugar, and caffeine. I was using food as medicine and avoided anything containing chemicals, hormones, or foods that might be genetically modified. I reasoned that if the FDA allowed drugs onto the market that held hidden dangers for at least some of us, who's to say just how safe processed foods could be. Eating healthier was difficult and it took a lot of time and effort to do the preparation day after day. On top of that, good, local food was expensive while prepackaged, convenience "foods" that were sugar-laden and toxic were affordable.

At this time I once again gave up coffee and focused on calming teas. I usually drank chamomile or peppermint, but also grew various herbs and even explored herbal and medicinal, albeit legal, smoking blends.

I also decided to slowly taper off the low dose of Seroquel, wondering if I might be having a tolerance withdrawal type of reaction to it. I discussed with Beth my ongoing efforts at sleep hygiene. I reported the changes I was making at work and at home to lessen others' reliance upon me. These massive efforts clearly had an over-the-top quality, but I was desperate for an answer. I could not keep going as I had been without sleep.

Eventually I shared what had happened to me in the medical and mental health systems. Beth was very non-committal. She seemed, like many therapists, to leave the focus on psychiatric drugs to the doctors. By this time I was so determined to change my situation through my own efforts that what she thought or didn't think about my story didn't really matter to me.

Journal Entry

December 13, 1997

Suicide. Do I have to tell you how tired I am of hanging on?

Pain. Who knows why I feel this pain and what to do about it.

Kids. If only I could push out of my mind the realities they face if I do.

Pain. If only I could push out of my mind the realities I face if I don't.

Suicide. Sweet, sweet suicide. Just the thought releases so much.

I'm still taking Remron and Klonopin. Nothing is working. Society is going to shit and who cares? This way of living really galls me. Our post-industrial, capitalistic, selfish, survival of the fittest society. When you make it you make it, and when you don't it's a story nobody will even know or care about.

CONSEQUENCES

After I got off of the medications, I began reading books and articles on the relationship between doctors and pharmaceutical companies to better understand what had happened to me and why. I became familiar with the names of several doctors who were going public with some uncomfortable truths about what they were discovering in connection with pharmaceutical company marketing of medications that resulted in devastating effects for many individuals and their families.

One of those was Dr. David Healy, an internationally respected psychiatrist, psychopharmacologist, scientist, and author. Having written his Ph.D. thesis on the seratonin re-uptake system, Dr. Healy had quickly understood the usefulness of the SSRI anti-depressants soon after they were developed. He was a university professor and one of the world's leading psychiatrists. He was also an expert on anti-depressants. In his practice, he put a large number of patients on drugs like Prozac and Paxil and found that while they were suitable for many, they were harmful for others. From the early nineties research had suggested that medications like Prozac caused some people to have suicidal urges. Around 1999, he began conducting studies to see if he could find out who would and would not be at risk while using SSRIs. This, he said, was a prerequisite to prescribing the drugs responsibly. By the year 2000, he was one of only a handful of scientists who continued to investigate suicide in connection with SSRIs because he believed patients needed to know how these drugs could affect them.

He contended that if a drug like Prozac caused people to commit suicide at a rate of one in 1,000, that might not seem like such a bad risk. But if 50 million people were put on the drug which resulted in 50,000 suicides, that would be no small disaster. Drug manufacturers like Eli Lilly were not conducting studies to determine which patients the drugs might not be suitable for. They had studies that indicated the drugs could be a good treatment for depression and that was enough for them.

In November of 2000, Dr. Healy accepted a prestigious job offer at one of Canada's top research centers, the University of Toronto. He was to head the Centre for Addiction and Mental Health. However, following a lecture he gave in which he mentioned the need for further research in regard to drugs like Prozac, the job offer was abruptly rescinded.

In the lecture, he had also touched on conflicts of interest between medical doctors and pharmaceutical companies and about the imperative need to minimize drug company influence on doctors. Although this lecture had been rated higher by audience members than that of any other speaker, afterward, the department decided his approach was not compatible with the program's goals.

The university maintained that there was no valid scientific evidence to prove the drugs could cause suicide and that Healy's suggestion otherwise raised questions about his ability as a doctor. He was described by some at the time as being scientifically irresponsible. At the American Foundation for Suicide Prevention, Dr. Charles Nemeroff, who was Chair of the Department of Psychiatry at Atlanta's prestigious Emory University and a paid consultant to a dozen drug companies, denounced Dr. Healy as basically being "a nut."

Dr. Healy later discovered that the department he had been invited to become director of received 52 percent of its funding for research from none other than drug companies. The corporate donations included $1.5 million from Eli Lilly, the maker of Prozac. The drug companies, as described by one doctor, were the mortar in the walls of the medical establishment. It would seem that the job offer was withdrawn because the University did not want the role of pharmaceutical companies questioned in the shaping of their medical research.

8

Cornerstone

Lynn/February 2013

BETH WENT ON MATERNITY leave in early 2013 and I was given a new therapist, Lynn. I was fine with the change because the type of support I had been receiving was less like therapy and more like symptom management. It helped to stay on track with my life and goals if I talked to someone about things every few weeks.

Lynn seemed fresh out of the box. She had a potted philodendron growing on the windowsill, her university certificates hanging neatly on the wall, and a small bookshelf filled with strategies for helping clients like me. She was skilled at listening to what I had to say and reflecting that back to me. It felt good to talk to someone who made an effort to understand, especially in the case of my history in the mental health system. When the measures I was taking were not producing the sleep I was so actively working for, I expressed frustration about both the likelihood that my insomnia was due to former medications, and the lack of concern for my welfare by the current system.

She seemed to get it, but she was also at a loss to do anything about it. She was a therapist, not a doctor, and medication matters were not her usual focus. Still, she did reflect my frustration back to me and also seemed to understand it: that I felt I had been hurt in a system that could now offer me nothing. That was something. For the most part, she was supportive of my goals. At one point I tried to do some trauma processing with her, but she seemed as if she lacked training. She didn't have a predictable method, and a few times the session was over before I'd had a chance to rebalance emotionally. I was committed to addressing these events from my childhood, but I just wouldn't be doing it with her.

. . . .

I really liked my grandma, although after a certain point I wasn't allowed to keep in touch with her. Whenever she saw me she would say, "Well, Laura Ann!" and hurried over to give me a big hug and a kiss. Sometimes she would give me two kisses, one on each cheek. My grandma loved me, and that was rare in my family.

One summer, I was allowed to visit her house in Rossville for a whole week. The other kids were at 4-H camp and my stepmom must have wanted me out of her hair. Mostly, Grandma and I just hung out. She had a garden in the back yard and an apple tree; my job was to help her gather the apples that had fallen to the ground. She had boxes full of them. That was it. That was my work for the day. Compared to the loitering I would've been stuck doing at my house, this was Paradise.

I didn't know what a hoarder was, but she had sold Avon and kept piles of it, so she dug out a kids' pink bath mitt and some soap for me to take home. Every day I patiently waited until she decided it was time to get into the deep freeze for some strawberry ice cream, or to scrounge up some of the Heath or Milky Way candy bars I knew she had stashed in the drawers of her kitchen. Then, a few hours later, she would scrounge up some of her other goodies. At dinnertime we got to eat in her living room, sitting amidst the piles of papers, boxes, and books, while she watched the TV news. There was a bearded hippie with unwashed hair talking about marijuana. Grandma said he had a thick tongue and sounded like he spoke with a mouth full of mashed potatoes. She turned the channel. She didn't like him. She had a *Reader's Digest Bible Picture Book* for me to look at, comfy couch pillows with crocheted covers, and walls decorated with several amateur paintings she had done herself. After dinner I got to take long, luxurious Avon bubble baths.

The best thing about being at Grandma's, though, was that I could relax. My stepmom didn't like it, but once in a while she ended up doing something for herself that inadvertently turned out to be a bonanza for me. This was one of those times and I relished it. We both knew there would be plenty of suffering just as soon as she got me home. When she came to pick me up, I asked her if the other kids were home from camp yet. I knew better than to say it, but it would be easier on my stomach if I knew on the ride home that there would be other kids there for her to pick on. She smiled at Grandma and told me they were. The car door shut and the harangue began. It was rude, she said, to only want to be at Grandma's because the other kids were at 4-H camp.

Grandma came to our house for dinner once in a while, mostly in the summertime. The one particular time that I remember was when I was between the fourth and fifth grade. My stepmom was off somewhere, so it was fun. My dad, Grandma, me and a couple of my brothers were eating off of thin paper plates and I remember we had baked beans with salad, and maybe hot dogs or hamburgers. Dad and Grandma continued to sit at the table visiting, drinking beer and iced tea after everyone had finished eating. Most of the kids had scattered. An argument ensued that ended with Dad taking one of the soggy paper plates and smearing the leftover food into his own mother's face. She got up and walked out, face dripping. My stepmom came home and he told her all about it. I wouldn't see Grandma again for years.

My dad and stepmom had an alliance that was never stronger than when they were pointing the finger at someone else. The one thing they could always agree upon was that they had an enemy. My mom. Us kids. The neighbor's dog. This time it just happened to be Grandma. But when they weren't ganging up on somebody, their relationship became a raging, autoimmune disaster. When pressures mounted that couldn't be released by hating their enemies, they turned on each other, unleashing their own pernicious Hell.

First they had the pre-fight. This was the fight before the Fight. If you missed out on the pre-fight, you hadn't missed much. It was simply the stage that sent dad out to drink. We kids could decipher when dad had left for town because the house would become eerily quiet. Oddly, my stepmom was home yet no one was being picked on.

She sat peacefully in her chair by the lamp, reading the *Farmer's Almanac* and acting as if she were merely waiting on a package to arrive. She did, however, suggest to us kids that we might want to hit the sheets early.

When my dad went out drinking, I imagined him passing through the swinging doors of the Long Branch Saloon and taking his seat next to Marshall Dillon at the bar. He was thirsty. I could hear the old Wurlitzer piano playing while Miss Kitty served him straight up whiskey, and also heard the mirror shatter when he hurled his glass on the way out.

He arrived home loaded and parked his truck up in the yard, leaving the lights on. I was in my bed, lights off, waiting for the terror to begin. While my stepmom was never more confident in her determination to control the alcoholic, I huddled under my covers developing avoidant personality disorder. He hadn't been inside the house for long before he cracked my door open, flipped on the light, and stuck his head in. I peeked out from my blankets; he looked like a red-faced Mr. Toad. He shut the door and was gone.

While there wasn't any lamb's blood sprinkled on my doorway to explain this miraculous passover, there was a fair amount of dried blood my stepmom had left running down the wall after she accidentally smacked her bandaged hand while yanking me around by my hair. (She had sliced herself good while cutting up a chicken and made sure I understood whose fault the retraumatization was, leaving the splattered blood as a reminder). Nah, I was just lucky.

What happened from there was just the usual, boring stuff: children crying at being dragged from their beds, grown-ups yelling and fighting all up and down the hallway, doors slamming, furniture crashing and dishes breaking, although I couldn't tell you any specifics. I was minding my own business laying neatly in my bed, like a nutcracker.

The day after these fights their alliance would be rekindled, stronger than ever. Things returned to normal which meant they got back to work focusing on us kids. I wasn't the only kid who caught it but when I did, even when I was older, my heart beat inside my chest like a tiny bunny rabbit's.

He was at the breakfast table. I was around fifteen. He'd had some Shredded Wheat and a large slice of cantaloupe and now the thin rind sat there on his plate, pulverized and puddled with juice. He was finished with it so he could start in on me. He ordered me to sit down. While I don't remember what it was that I had done, I do remember him calling me, "Sister Sue," something he liked to say when he was at his most combustible.

Another thing he liked to do was ask questions like, "Who raised you, anyway?" Clueless as I was, I had to pause and think about it. I had to be careful at how I answered these questions.

"You did," came to mind, but if I said that it might set him off because he was clearly upset with me and wouldn't tolerate being insulted for having raised such a disappointing child.

"Who raised you!" he repeated.

Taking time to think was not a particularly useful skill in our family. I struggled in my mind. If I said "Mom did," he would definitely blow because that wasn't even the truth and he hated Mom. I vacillated between the two options unable to think of any others.

"Who raised you, god damn it!" He was already ablaze.

"I don't know," I said, because I truly did not know how to reply to his question.

"I did, god damn you! I raised you!"

Hello Grandma. The slimy cantaloupe rind glided nicely over my cheeks and nose, from my forehead to my chin. The juice was not as cool as I would have liked it, and not as sweet as some I have tasted. It did leave a refreshing aroma in my hair, but a little sticky, and nothing as splendid as I could have had from Avon. All in all I was rather disappointed, but since the apple had fallen so far from the tree, I might hope one could do so again.

Those fuckers were frightening. Clearly warped human beings, malfunctioning. She was stuck in overdrive and always the worst, but I was more afraid of him, even as an adult. She could catch you off guard, but you always *knew* she had it out for you. Not a sane thought in her head. He might be laughing at your jokes one minute and have you by the throat the next, cracking your head against the kitchen cabinets. I suppose they were broken, maybe fractured in childhood, and these were the manifestations of their inner turmoil. Predictable responses to invisible stimuli. Sick people on automatic pilot, and children brought out the worst in them. Children, for fuck's sake.

We were powerless. As children we were. That's why they hurt us, because they could. They finally had power over somebody and, by god, we'd do it their way or else. It was their turn to shine, their turn to call the shots. To be important. And what better way to feel important than to hurtfully dominate a child?

It was a tremendous need they had, to make regular deposits, regular dumps of garbage into beings more powerless than they were. It was their food, their nourishment, and they fed off their young. Like a true horror movie, when one child left home, their attention riveted to the others. When the last child was gone, they turned on each other, to devour the other. The Demons had run out of playthings. Abruptly, they hatefully parted ways, started new and exciting lives, and lived as if none of it had happened.

. . . .

Lynn and I focused on my present day goals. In early fall of 2012, I had begun volunteer work at a local community garden and farmer's market. I had hoped that by doing work I enjoyed, I might experience less stress and gain the skills needed to find employment in an area that I had a passion for. I liked the idea of people producing their own food in their own neighborhoods. Oil was said to be running out, and I wondered if the era of foods being transported over thousands of miles might be a blip on the screen in the history of human societies. No matter what race or nationality, all of our ancestors had fended for themselves in this way, and I was hoping to see things get back to normal. The last grocery store had moved out of this particular neighborhood about five years earlier, and while it may have been a pipe dream, I was looking forward to the day local efforts would make it to where Kroger and Save-a-Lot stores would no longer be needed.

While I gained great experience doing everything from record-keeping to growing kale and radishes, in the spring of 2013, I experi-

58

enced so much sleeplessness that I began breaking down socially. I pushed myself to go no matter how sleep deprived I was only to end up saying and doing odd things and completely embarrassing myself.

One afternoon, I had been asked to assist other volunteers in the community kitchen. We had juiced beets that day, and being someone who used a juicer regularly, I wanted to show the high school kid who was doing clean-up how he could thoroughly clean the inside of the juicer. I quickly scanned the storeroom for a brush and found one two shelves below the tea towels and plastic baggies. When I tried to hand it to him, he hesitated and then said, "No, I've got this."

I insisted, saying it would help him get the food particles out of the mesh screen. He hesitated again and then finally said, "I think that's a toilet bowl brush."

Yep. I was instructing him to clean the juicer with a toilet bowl brush. True, I had found it on a lower shelf in a food closet, but it had, in fact, been used on toilets. I was humiliated. It seemed no matter what I tried, no matter if I did or didn't take Seroquel, I couldn't get adequate sleep. And sometimes the results manifested themselves gloriously like they had on that day.

Between May and August of 2013, I had gone completely off of Seroquel. Despite all efforts, severe sleep problems remained. I told Lynn I would need to see a psychiatrist to resume taking medication and I told her I didn't want to see Dr. Elliot. I thought perhaps a new psychiatrist might have a new idea.

Lynn made an appointment for me with the new psychiatrist, and that's when things really began going downhill.

Journal Entry

January 4, 1998

I'm still struggling. I don't know how much of this de-pression is physical illness and how much is due to cir-cumstances. I feel pain, but at least I am living. At least I am feeling. I am alive and for some reason the fact that I feel, even pain, gives me hope.

In social work practice we learned about tapping cli-ent motivation. People need to be shown that their actions can make a difference. We also talked about full and equitable employment, about the value of having a good job.

I have decided to take a semester off of school and re-turn to drywall full-time where I can work and feel pro-ductive. Arnold asked me to head the sanding crew. It's a challenge and I will learn new things. The hours are bet-ter than the job at Kansas Children's Service League would have been and he understands my needs as a moth-er. I've had a positive mental attitude so far. Socially I'm putting myself forward. I want to do that more.

Village Behavioral Health

Oakley, Laurie A.
Progress Notes
January 7, 1998
Hour: 3:15
Length: 15
Goal Progress: Fair – Good

Narrative Summary: Client reports she decreased Remeron to 15 mg. She tried stopping it, but found herself more anxious. She is taking a semester off from school and working sanding drywall. She likes the physical exercise.

9

Cornerstone

Dr. Lantz/September 2013

D R. LANTZ APPEARED VERY busy. He was younger than Dr. Elliot, which I thought may have accounted for the difference in the way he approached clients. Dr. Lantz didn't look at or face me. He sat at his desk with papers and pen, busily reviewing information and writing things down. When he did look up it was merely a public speaking type gesture. He looked briefly at the space above my head before turning back to his desk.

I tried to summarize my history as simply as I could. It was difficult because I wasn't sure if he was hearing anything I said. He didn't really respond to my story, just sifted through papers and wrote things down. Finally, I gave up. I sat in my chair staring at the potted plant until he was ready to engage.

He didn't ask any questions about me. He didn't want to know if I'd had thoughts of harming myself or others, or if I'd had temper outbursts or any fun. He only wanted to talk about medication. And oddly, he was less concerned with the benefits and risks of medications than he was with what they cost.

He was big on Trazodone, an older anti-depressant that makes you sleepy. It was cheap and relatively safe, he said. A lot of doctors prescribed it for insomnia. I told him I had tried Trazodone a few years earlier after Dr. Elliot had prescribed it on a trial basis. The first dose made me feel so heavy and clouded the next day that I had a hard time getting off to work. I decided not to keep taking it.

He said those effects were common with most people and it might take some time to adjust. Since I had switched from Dr. Elliot hoping to find new solutions, I agreed to give Trazodone another try. I got the prescription filled, however I decided not to take it when I read it could exacerbate my heart arrhythmia. While both insomnia and Seroquel were bad for your heart, I didn't want to add anything new to the mix. The truth was, I had a long history of not getting along as well as others on medications, and didn't want to risk making the heart arrhythmia worse.

. . . .

I had begun to notice the arrhythmia when I was 17 or 18, but it was rare. Then, when I was 25 and pregnant with my first child, Grace, it started happening more. Wayne, her father, accompanied me to one of my visits to the obstetrician where I mentioned that it was occurring more frequently. I noticed it mostly when I was laying on my left side; it felt like a pause, or sometimes a quiver, and then it would beat regularly again. This was before all the commercials, yet I was already inclined to "talk to my doctor."

"Just don't lay on your left side," he said, smiling, looking at Wayne. They both laughed. A few weeks later I went into labor with Grace. At the hospital, he made it to the room as I was crying out, just about to deliver. Flat on my back with feet in the stirrups, he stood gazing at me from the foot of the table, his face glowing with a distinct, power-trippy pleasure. *Huh.* He was getting something out of this. I guess male obstetricians had other reasons for choosing the profession besides getting to look at vaginas all day.

I never gave my arrhythmia much thought after that. We had our second child, Marley, two years later, and then divorced when Marley was three. Social workers at the Battered Women's Task Force assured me that Wayne alone was responsible for his behavior, but I knew I'd had a part. Once, he told me I fought the nastiest and meanest of any woman he had known. I just figured he didn't like hearing the truth. But I knew I had a mouth. I also knew Grace and Marley would not grow up in the kind of home that I'd grown up in. We'd been through the cycle a thousand times: the big blow-up, the I'm sorry it'll never happen again, on to the honeymoon until the tension built once more, and then another blow-up, always bigger than the last. I was unwilling to do it again.

After the divorce, our relationship began to revolve around our shared custody of the kids. He was angry, and we fought constantly, but he was always there for them. He didn't take off and he didn't move on. He picked them up from school two or three days a week and took them out for supper or back to his house. He had them every other weekend and took them to museums, and parks, or to visit his family and friends. He rode the school bus with them on field trips and volunteered in their classrooms. He was always there for his kids.

It was a Sunday evening in September of 2000 when he called to say he was sick and would not be able to pick them up the next day. He said after we hung up he would be driving himself back to St. Francis Hospital where he had been on Thursday and was checked out before being sent back home. He said he had been having chest pains since then and was burning up. He hadn't slept since Tuesday, hadn't eaten since Wednesday, and had thrown up repeatedly. Before hanging up, I asked if he wanted to talk to Grace. For the first time ever, he said no. While he hadn't been nice, for the first time since our break-up he wasn't the least bit hateful toward me. Something had to be very wrong.

Early on the following morning, our friend who worked at the hospital called me. "Wayne's had a massive heart attack and was moved to ICU this morning," she said. "You should probably bring the kids." He was only forty-four. He had stopped smoking in 1988, the year that I met him. Although he tended to order most of his meals out, he swam and biked regularly, kept an eye on his cholesterol numbers, and was not one pound overweight. We were all shocked.

A stent was placed and a month later he was sent home with instructions, among other things, to never again shovel snow. A large portion of his heart was dead. I would drop the kids off and return to pick them up until he was given the okay to drive. By this time, late fall of 2000, I had recovered from the pharmaceutical misadventure that had nearly caused me to take my life, although I was still on med-

65

ications and felt somewhat "off." He and I never talked about it. Since the divorce, we hadn't really been on speaking terms, just fighting terms. His medical crisis didn't change that. As his strength returned, so did his disdain for me. This was normal. Soon, he would return to his job at the Frito Lay plant where he had spent long hours on his feet, tossing boxes of Doritos onto pallet boards.

His problem had never been with his heart, but always with his feet. He had put in over ten years at the plant. I'd guessed he had spent more of his paychecks on trying different insoles and special shoes than his corporate bosses had spent on golf clubs. When we were married, I was forever giving him foot rubs and fixing up foot baths for him to soak in. After we split, he began going to doctors regularly for different kinds of treatments for his painful feet.

The officer used the word *deceased* twice. Once on the phone when I was notified at work, and again in the doorway of our mobile home as he handed me the glasses that were crushed when the cardiac event occurred. Marley's eyes followed the bent glasses, his mouth hanging open. He and Grace were seven and nine, and present when the sheriff gave his report. The deceased had been found lying face down in his home. His buddy Rick performed CPR, as did the paramedics, but there was nothing that could be done. He assured us their dad was probably well-gone before his face hit the floor.

Grace had a weak immune system and spent the next few days at home, vomiting into a bucket. Marley boarded the school bus the next morning like it was a regular day. When I went to pick him up, the lunch room monitor, Paula, said she overheard him tell the other second-graders that his dad had died but was being fixed and would soon come back. Also overheard at a different time was him saying he would get a new dad.

Grace felt better in time for the visitation. As family members gathered in the dim lit sanctuary, she lingered near the open casket with her aunts, cradling one of the dozens of teddy bears that had been dropped off at the house by the friends and acquaintances who had brought food, feeling helpless to do more. As those who remembered Wayne filtered in and out of the room, there were hugs, tears, and an occasional, soothing chuckle.

Marley wanted no part of it, so he and I hung out in an adjacent room, being silly. "Would you like some coffee?" the funeral director approached me and offered.

"Okay, sure," said Marley. Marley didn't even drink coffee. At least not until that day.

I have to be honest. For me, losing their dad was complicated. It was like winning the Powerball and being dropped in the Sahara Desert without shoes. Simultaneously. Anyone who knew us, who knew Wayne, knew I'd earned every right to be euphorically relieved. Like a thick, taut rubber band, my patience had been stretched for years by his continual animosity; even though it felt amazing to be free from the tension, I knew I'd be mangled when it finished snapping back. My kids and I had been dealt a dreadful blow. It would be a long road back to nowhere-near-normal and every bridge would be out.

. . . .

My decision not to take Trazodone was, in part, guided by the reality my kids and I faced when someone we loved was perfectly healthy one minute and was irreversibly gone the next. For me, the words, "a risk of worsening heart arrhythmia," were not just small print or fast talk at the tale end of a pharmaceutical advertisement, but a very real possibility. I was 48 years old, had already been experiencing the arrhythmia more often, and while my quality of life was significantly compromised by insomnia, I knew how much worse things could get on the wrong medication. I did not want to risk that. This information was not welcome with Dr. Lantz. I would soon learn the price I would pay for exercising my own judgment where medications are concerned.

Journal Entry

February 9, 1998

Life is good. Working drywall full-time has literally saved me. I love my job, I love life, I am working out my problems. I'm taking Remron but not as much. I still take Klonpin, but the exercise I get working at drywall every day is what I think is pulling me out of depression.

Not exactly success as our culture defines it, but I do feel better now even though I quit school. I've given up "making it" in an educational sense. Still, I am grateful. At least now I can celebrate life in the simple everyday with my kids.

EXERCISE RX

While the design methods of earlier studies were found some-what lacking, by 1993, carefully conducted studies were part of a growing body of evidence that showed depression and anxiety could be more successfully treated by incorporating exercise into an indi-vidual's treatment plan.

Researchers found that it doesn't take intense exercise to see a benefit, nor did patients need to reach any physical fitness goals. A simple regimen of walking, working up to 20 to 30 minutes a session, 3 days a week, was sufficient to produce positive effects. While more intensive exercise was associated with higher rates of remission, the drop-out rate for these participants was also higher. Those who stayed with the exercise program for 9 weeks or longer saw the most im-provement, and at 10 months regular exercise was a significant pre-dictor of an improved outcome. These benefits were seen despite dif-ferences in age, gender, and severity of depression. Moderate exercise was found to be "just as beneficial and not significantly different from psychotherapy, pharmacologic therapy, and other behavioral interven-tions," stated researchers Craft and Landers at the conclusion of their analysis.

Exercise has also been compared in studies to psychotropic medication. In the late 1990's, Duke psychologist, James Blumenthal, was the lead researcher in a study of 156 moderately depressed men and women who were randomly assigned to either exercise, medica-tion, or both. At the end of the 16 week study, exercise was found to be as effective as medication, and a 10 month follow-up revealed the ex-ercise participants had more successful maintenance of remission from depression than those in either the medication-only or combination groups.

Despite the fact that remission rates for those on SSRI medica-tions and other commonly used drugs for mood disorders are only around 30 percent, doctors have traditionally overlooked prescribing exercise in the same way one would prescribe medication. One of the reasons given is because while studies indicate that exercise improves mood, the mechanisms behind that outcome are not yet understood.

Dr. Madhukar H. Trivedi, a professor of psychiatry at the University of Texas Southwestern Medical Center in Dallas, is one doctor who has prescribed exercise as seriously as one would prescribe medication. He became interested in treating patients with exercise after several of his patients who were not fully responding to SSRI medications reported they felt better after taking walks. Dr. Trivedi and his colleagues oversaw a study in which exercise was prescribed as formal medicine instead of adding another drug like lithium or an antipsychotic. Patients were monitored in the same way they would have been had they been prescribed a pill.

The study, which was published in *The Journal of Clinical Psychiatry* in May of 2011, reported a remission rate of 29.5 percent. Dr. Trivedi concluded, "I think that our results indicate that exercise is a very valid treatment option." The success rate was equal to or better than that of other back-up treatments for those not fully responding to SSRI's.

A 2012 report by the Centers for Disease Control showed that while more doctors are advising their overweight or obese patients to participate in physical activity, exercise therapy is an uncommon recommendation for most adults. It is not yet standard practice among physicians to prescribe exercise for patients with chronic physical conditions like type 2 diabetes, heart disease, high blood pressure, and cancer, let alone those seeking treatment for psychiatric conditions.

Though it can be difficult to stay motivated when dealing with depression, individuals need to be informed that exercise is a legitimate treatment option. Side effects are nearly non-existent while the cost is minimal. The added health benefits of cardiovascular fitness and disease reduction compare favorably to the potential risk of side-effects associated with antidepressant medication.

I don't remember my exact motivation for returning to drywall construction, but a combination of factors including consistent, daily exercise eventually lifted me out of the suicidal depression. In school I had been accumulating debt which contributed to my stress, whereas drywall work provided me with a steady paycheck. My supervisor was a caring individual who showed me a great deal of respect and also put me in charge of a work crew. This boosted my faltering self-esteem. That first few weeks while remaining suicidal it surprised me how normally I was able to function despite being secretly at significant risk. Thankfully, by six to eight weeks I was out of the woods.

PART TWO

THE CONFLICT

"When your only tool is a hammer,
all problems look like nails."

— *The Law of the Instrument*

10

Cornerstone

Dr. Lantz/November 2013

I 'M NOT GOING TO LIE and say my only motivation for seeing Dr. Lantz was for medication, though it was true that I needed medication if I wanted to sleep. Neither did I have high hopes that he would have any solutions that Dr. Elliot didn't. But he was a doctor. When you have a health problem, a doctor is a good place to start.

My secondary motivation was to have a record. My ability to work and to function was significantly affected by a chronic lack of sleep. I first realized in 2007 that if I wasn't in the system and establishing that record, I was cutting myself off from the social security safety net I had been paying into my entire working life under the assumption that if I became unable to support myself, it would be there.

Qualifying for disability requires statements from a doctor attesting to the facts of your condition. I was seeking treatment for insomnia, for sure. But by early 2013, I had already addressed the problem for nearly ten years. Because treatment efforts had failed, I had been forced to scale back on work repeatedly, sold my car and our three-family house, lived without health insurance, quit paying the life insurance policies I'd had for the kids and myself for several years, plowed through each day supporting others without ever getting enough restorative rest for myself, and on most days (and nights), en-ured the TMJ headaches, fatigue, bruxism, and memory and cognition difficulties that had gone along with it. By the time I saw Dr. Lantz, I admit, I was shamefully ready to file.

I never brought up disability with Dr. Lantz. I was truly inter-ested in knowing if he had a viable option. I knew it was a long shot, and I knew there were a lot of medications I wouldn't risk taking. I was sure he would understand when I told him about the serious reactions I'd had on meds and all of the ways in which this had affected my life. I wanted him to know my situation and thereby gain his support.

But in working with Dr. Lantz, the focus became Trazodone. He prescribed it and I had gotten the prescription filled but had not taken it. I told him I decided not to take it because I have a heart ar-rhythmia and one side-effect Trazodone might cause is a worsening of that condition. He rarely made eye contact, but when I told him this, he did as he let out a defeated sigh and challenged me to tell him how much coffee I drink in a day.

When I told him I have one cup in the morning, he questioned me further as if he didn't believe me. Then he stated that if I wanted to continue my prescription of Seroquel, I was "gonna have to pay" for blood tests. I realized most people who take Seroquel needed health monitoring, but no doctor had ever required me to have tests because I had never taken more than the absolute lowest dose. At this point I was taking one fourth the lowest dose. So I repeated his words, "gonna have to pay?"

We made eye contact for a second time. He tilted his head back and looking down reminded me that I'd told him I didn't have health insurance. Then he repeated that I would have to pay for the tests. I didn't get it. I barely knew this man and he didn't know me. I wondered if he hated his job. Stuck indoors all day in an undecorated office, his skin was pale and he was slightly overweight. I was begin-ning to wonder if the job was getting to him, or maybe he had prob-lems at home. The one thing I did know was that he didn't exactly have it together with me.

The tests wouldn't be a problem at the clinic I go to. I told him it would cost me 25 dollars and they would treat me with more respect than he just had. This softened him a bit and he scribbled out the prescription for Seroquel as well as an order for blood tests.

Journal Entry

May 10, 1998

Sunday the kids and I went to church and I just sat there unable to remember anyone's name. The preacher mentioned Harry S. Truman in the sermon and I thought he was referring to a movie star. Last night my sister and I went to a movie and once again I had trouble following the story line. Today my neighbor is waxing her car and I realize after almost two years that the thing isn't dark green, it's black.

Now when I think of these things I get a sinking feeling. What has happened to fry my brain? When I told the nurse practitioner, Vicki, that I couldn't remember if it was spring or fall, she started me back on Zyprexa. I am to continue taking Remron and Klonopin.

My job has really helped balance my moods for the past four months. I hope to find something to put me back where I need to be mentally.

What's important? The kids and me. And loving people.

THE MAINE BENZODIAZEPINE
STUDY GROUP

What first comes to mind when one hears the word benzo-diazepine, or the names of drugs like Valium and Klonopin, is addiction. This is a long-standing, incomplete public perception fostered by drug company interests that hides an ongoing medical nightmare while making the corporate drug cartels and their stockholders rich.

What should come to mind when you think of these drugs are consequences as severe as brain damage in individuals who take what are considered therapeutic doses as prescribed by their doctors. While only a minority of users end up with true drug addiction, the generally accepted pattern of longer-term prescribing leaves millions with an iatrogenic (doctor caused) physiological dependence that chains them to the medical system as their mental and physical health slowly deteriorates.

With this in mind, in 2002, a group of medical professionals from several US states, Canada, and the UK, met in Bangor Maine to form a study group that subsequently gathered data on benzodiazepine use to consider evidence-based strategies that might promote appropriate prescribing and usage.

The Maine Benzodiazepine Study Group then authored several fact sheets for healthcare and policy professionals, as well as for the general population. A set of guidelines for prescribing were also put forth that took into account the many adverse outcomes for patients who continued to be prescribed these medications in countries all over the world.

This was a fresh and appreciable effort toward addressing a problem that was anything but new. The first benzodiazepines had been developed by the early 1960's, and even then some researchers were noticing potential problems that warranted further study. These studies were never undertaken and instead, the drugs were marketed as being safe compared to the older drugs they would replace.

While benzodiazepines were safer in some respects, by 1980, so many in the UK were experiencing adverse effects of the drugs that there was a public uproar. These were also widely prescribed block-buster drugs in US, yet there was not the same public recognition of the problem. Again, what *was* recognized was drug addiction, something that could be blamed on individuals who were unable to control their cravings for drugs.

In reality, benzodiazepines do nothing less than disable the brain. They are, at first, sedating. Tolerance sets in rather quickly, usually within the first two weeks. Fine judgment and memory impairments often occur and continue despite tolerance. The learning and retention of new information is often inhibited, partly because taking the drugs leads to a lack of concentration and attention. Episodic memory, that of recalling recent events, when and where they occurred, and their sequence of time, can be moderately to severely disrupted. Uncharacteristic behavior is often observed.

Studies have shown that benzodiazepines can both cause and aggravate depression. Emotional blunting, where a person does not feel their full range of emotions, is common. People who are treated long-term with these medications often pass through important periods of their lives unable to feel pleasure or pain or to fully enjoy their relationships with family members and others.

While memory and cognition continue to be affected, anxiety will return. For those who do not seek an increased dosage, a paradoxical reaction is common in which anxiety becomes worse than it had been originally. Even so, only a minority of patients seek larger and larger doses until a true addiction develops.

Persons who take benzodiazepines, especially the elderly, are at a higher risk of accidents. Fatal overdoses can occur when they are combined with other drugs. (Think Michael Jackson and Heath Ledger, two well-known individuals who both died in desperate attempts to get a good night's sleep). The risks of suicide are higher for depressed persons taking benzodiazepines. There are also increased risks of aggressive or uncharacteristic behavior, auto accidents, job loss, and absenteeism because of illness. There are adverse effects for both pregnant mothers and their newborn babies. Effects ranging from lowered quality of life to a gradual deterioration of mental and physical health are common among persons prescribed this class of drugs.

In 1994, Professor Heather Ashton of the UK, an expert in the field of pharmacological studies and on the effects of benzodiazepines in particular, set forth and published, *Guidelines for the Rational Use of Benzodiazepines*. Unfortunately, standard prescribing practices and practitioner attitudes toward this class of drugs are so well ingrained in medical culture that Dr. Ashton's recommendations have not gained much recognition.

What Professor Ashton and the Maine Benzodiazepine Study Group has set forth is this: while the benzodiazepine class of drugs are effective medicines with several uses, longer-term usage (taken regularly for more than 2 – 4 weeks), can lead to a myriad of problems. Benzodiazepines are most safely used intermittently or for a very few days. Longer-term prescribing should only be considered in situations that cannot be solved by other means, and only then when it is determined that the benefit outweighs the many risks.

Unfortunately, longer-term prescribing of benzodiazepines remains an accepted, standard practice worldwide, and in some places such as South Africa and India, they are even available over-the-counter. After a natural disaster, prescription drug donations often flood affected areas, and because of a lack of regulation, many who receive them experience a prolonged and even more personal disaster.

11

Cornerstone

Pre-Appointment Journal Entry
November 16, 2013

I NEED TO JOURNAL BEFORE my appointment. I don't quite know why I am even going. Bottom line: I feel they do not respect me there. This is the system that hurt me before. It matters to me. I've expressed it to them. They don't believe or disbelieve; it doesn't seem to matter to them. But that's not the only issue. Increasingly, they treat me more like a "client" than a real person. And how can I even call them on this because they have all the power. To them, I am a mental case so how could I know anything?

But I am not their judgments and lazy assumptions. They may not value me or believe me or respect me, but I do. Right now, I feel they see me as a problem because that protects them from the story I tell about the system, and indirectly about who they are and where they work and what it is they really do. The fact is, it's fucked up. They don't want to see that. It would cost them.

What do I need and can I get it there? I need Seroquel, or think I need it. I don't take much at all. Maybe doing yoga will bring about significant change, as well as the 12-Step recovery I am involved in. My upcoming work changes are actually creating some anxiety, because when I wake up around three and can't get back to sleep, I still have to get up at seven and go, whereas working at home I've had more flexibility and can sometimes get back to sleep.

I also need a paper trail in connection with a doctor that documents how chronic insomnia affects my daily life. Because it doesn't matter how great I look, or whether or not anyone thinks I'm trying to scam the system. Having access to a doctor is required if I need disability. I don't want to file right now, but taking care of myself means not closing the door on that option. And that's what I had done prior to 2007.

I want to be looking into where I might go in the future that might provide better care. I'm prepared to learn there isn't anything better, given my income. My income is about to drop again and I will probably only qualify for Medicaid. But it may be worth a shot. I've got my 12-step program, yoga, my higher power, myself, Nick, and the kids. I'm doing good. I can't let their judgments of me get me down. They can disbelieve me all they want, but I know what I tell them is true.

Journal Entry

January 22, 1999

Today I went to a new primary care doctor, Dr. Russell. I told him about my lack of energy and the difficulties I've been having with thinking and memory. He was surprised that I had been on Paxil, Prozac, Ascendin, Wellbutrin, and Effexor and that they had all caused panic attacks.

I asked if I could start getting my Serzone and Klonopin through his office so I wouldn't have to take off work early to get across town to the community mental health center. After asking many questions and treating me like an addict shopping for prescriptions, he told me to continue with my appointments across town.

I told him I had dropped out of my social work studies because of severe depression although I did manage to get an associates degree in criminal justice. Still, he treated me as an oddity and mocked my use of the word "cognitive." He seemed to marvel that I work in drywall and that I wear stilts for this. In the meantime he has ordered several tests.

No matter. My mission in life is to love my own children. That's all I care to accomplish.

RESEARCH

By the year 1999, when I was first figuring out something had seriously affected my brain, one would have thought more doctors might know something about the effects benzodiazepines have on cognitive function. After being introduced as wonder drugs around 1960, as early as 1975 some doctors were noticing patients who took drugs like Valium and Librium were having serious problems with memory and cognition.

I was prescribed Klonopin by practitioners whom I trusted as experts in their fields. I had no idea this medication was in the same class as and twenty times stronger than Valium. I had heard enough about Valium to know to stay away from it, not because of cognitive or memory effects, but what I had heard of addictive potential. Aside from having a different name, a half milligram dose of a medication didn't seem like much. Little did I know just how much damage this little pill could do.

While physicians are completely cognizant when it comes to the annoying drug seeking behavior of the benzodiazepine addicts who come to them for prescriptions, the majority of doctors just can't seem to wrap their heads around the other problems associated with these drugs that they and others in their profession have prescribed to millions.

This could be, in part, due to the fact that there are plenty of people for whom these drugs seem to pose very little problem. Each individual will metabolize a drug differently, and while many do quite well both taking and stopping a benzodiazepine, there are millions of others for whom it has not been so simple.

In 1982, Dr. Malcolm Lader, who was an expert on benzodiazepines at London's Institute of Psychiatry, reported at a conference in Washington state about research he had done on a group of individuals who were prescribed these medications for a number of years. Evidence from the brain scans of those who took therapeutic doses longer-term suggested their brains were damaged and shrunken when compared with scans of people who had not taken the drugs.

In 1989, one of his colleagues, anxiety specialist Isaac Marks, joined ten other eminent colleagues from research institutes in the United States, France, Germany, England, Spain, Portugal, and Brazil to publish a critique of the use of another benzodiazepine, Xanax, in the *Archives of General Psychiatry*. They reported "serious adverse effects" that only became apparent in time frames longer than clinical trials would have shown. Like Dr. Lader, they also found signs of brain atrophy in long-term users.

Interestingly, that critique was based in part on two studies that the maker of the drug had funded in the 1980's. These studies, also published in the *Archives of General Psychiatry*, showed that more than half of the patients experienced side-effects that might indicate neurological dysfunction. While these side-effects were downplayed or completely ignored by those conducting the pharmaceutical company studies, researchers like Lader and Marks were calling for more research.

As recently as 2010 there have been echos of a scandal in the UK because of previously unreleased secret documents revealing that the Medical Research Council had, in light of Dr. Lader's findings in 1982, recommended large-scale studies on the long-term impact of benzodiazepines on the brain. But as Dr. Heather Ashton wrote as recently as 2011, studies to investigate why so many long-term users display symptoms of functional brain damage have yet to be undertaken.

Studies that *are* being conducted were reported in March of 2014, in an article appearing in *Scientific American* titled, "Antianxiety Drugs Successfully Treat Autism." Researchers at the University of Washington are "excited" to find that a study they have recently done on mice suggests that core autistic behaviors can be effectively treated with benzodiazepines.

Results of this new study, that has now been published widely, were described as "encouraging," and are reported to have led to conversations among doctors about how to help their autistic patients by prescribing these drugs. One article predicts that parents may soon be asking doctors to prescribe benzodiazepines for their children even though they are not approved for treatment of autism.

In the study, mice showed noticeable improvements in social interaction, spatial learning, and a decrease in repetitive behaviors. Todd Scheuer, co-author of the study and a pharmacology research professor at the University of Washington stated, "The significance of this is that it uses drugs that are safe, that we already know so much about. It's a relatively simple—or conceptually simple—way to treat autism that seems to be effective."

The article goes on to say that these findings seem to substanti-ate a hypothesis that autistic behaviors are caused by chemical imbal-ances in the brain, and that a very low dose of a benzodiazepine, (Klonopin was used in the study), could correct that imbalance.

While it was acknowledged that the drugs may not be a good fit for everyone, it was reported that some clinicians already felt con-fident that they would be comfortable using this treatment for their autistic patients. Wendy Moyal, assistant medical director at New York Presbyterian Hospital's Center for Autism and the Developing Brain, noted a lack of drugs to treat the core symptoms of autism and stated, "This is a medication that has been around for a long time, and I know the effects and side-effects, so I feel comfortable using this medication off-label. These findings are exciting."

The research at Washington University was supported by the Simons Foundation, the National Institute of Child Health and Human Development, the National Institute of Neurological Disorders, and the National Institutes of Health. AstraZeneca and the National Institutes of Health have a clinical trial in human subjects underway to test whether the findings are relevant to humans.

For those of us who have been down a harrowing road of treat-ments with benzodiazepines, this "exciting" new development is noth-ing short of horrific. Clinical psychologist and author, Bruce Levine, pointed out in respect to antidepressants that the chemical imbalance theory has been repeatedly rejected by doctors who look closely at the research and find it lacking scientific legitimacy. I can only imagine that the chemical imbalance theory being used to support this drug treatment for individuals with autism is also what those doctors would call pseudoscientific.

In an interview for *Daily Kos,* Bruce Levine gave his take on that word. "'Pseudoscientific' is a polite term for the use of scientific-sounding language to promote unscientific realities. Less polite would be 'bullshit' or 'lies.'" In regard to these latest studies, those were my exact thoughts.

12

Cornerstone

Dr. Lantz/January 27, 2014

WAS I EARNING A REPUTATION for being difficult? I didn't know. Perhaps Dr. Lantz and I had just gotten off on the wrong foot. I very reluctantly decided to try Trazodone. When Dr. Elliot had prescribed it, I took the full amount but discontinued after the first dose when I felt completely drugged the following morning. Dr. Lantz was okay with me starting with a smaller amount.

I took it for three nights and hated it. Now, on top of functioning in spite of sleep deprivation, I had to endure the after-effects of a highly sedating drug while attempting to work. It also caused a similar mental fog as other medications I'd had trouble with. I'd learned the hard way to pay attention to how I felt on these drugs. Plus there were still the heart arrhythmia risks. So, I stopped taking it.

When I told Dr. Lantz, he turned back to his paperwork, let out an exasperated sigh, and set his pen down heavily. He said in his opinion, I should increase the dose over a two week period until I was taking a standard dose. Then I would sleep. I asked him if he remembered my history. He responded by saying he knew I had a fear of taking meds. I told him my fear was warranted given my past experiences. When I asked if it was important to him that he know me, and to know my history, he replied that what he knew was that millions of dollars and years of study went into the medications he prescribed. As he filled out the reminder card for my next appointment, I asked him to respond to my question of whether he was interested in knowing *me*. He said he did know me, and that my problem was a fear of taking medication.

This was my fourth session with him and already he had a pattern of interrupting and talking over me. I calmly told him that he and I were not a good fit and asked to be transferred to Dr. Elliot or another psychiatrist. Dr. Lantz said the agency didn't like clients making those kinds of changes and that I should seek treatment outside of the agency.

Before leaving, I asked if he had at least documented that I tried the medication. With the level of contempt he was targeting at me, I seriously doubted it. The fact was I tried it, mostly out of a desire to avoid being labeled non-compliant.

Dr. Lantz replied by saying he documented I had a fear of taking meds. I repeated the question: had he documented that I tried taking Trazodone. One of those rare occasions he actually looked me in the eye, he responded by saying, "I think you need to leave."

Journal Entry

March 29, 1999

This past week has been difficult. At drywall I had been rising above my pain. Now I have a back injury and cannot work. Why do I hold onto a belief that God should prevent hardship? I can count on God to let the hardship continue.

The medications don't really help that much but at least what I take now isn't causing major problems. Maybe that's better than nothing. When I asked Dr. Terrell for a muscle relaxer for my back, he told me I was already taking Klonopin. I didn't know that was a muscle relaxer and it doesn't work like the medication I was given a few years ago for my back. I went to my appointment wearing the back belt I bought at the medical supply where my sister works. Dr. Terrell asked who prescribed it and is treating me as if I'm faking. I switched to him for the closer location, but I was better off driving across town.

What can I do to keep it together mentally? Although I am unable to work right now, I still have something to give, I can make up for being scatterbrained by giving love, and I can love myself and accept that things are this way. I've got to quit trying to be how I think I ought to be and just be who I am.

93

Village Behavioral Health

Oakley, Laurie A.
Progress Notes
June 21, 1999
Hour: 3:30
Length: 15
Goal Progress: Good

Narrative Summary: Laurie is unable to go back to drywall work because of a back injury. She reports her mood and anxiety are quite satisfactory. She has taken up archery to manage her stress since she lost her job. Is now going to work with the developmentally disabled. Continue on meds as ordered.

13

Cornerstone

Lynn Final Session/January 27, 2014

I WAS SCHEDULED TO SEE Lynn right after my appointment with Dr. Lantz. I walked back out to the lobby and checked in at the front desk before sitting down. I couldn't believe what had just happened.

When Lynn called me back, I told her how Dr. Lantz had treated me and that he had let me go. She responded by asking me why I wanted to see a psychiatrist if I won't take medication. She had asked me this question in a previous session, and I couldn't understand how it escaped her that I did, in fact, take Seroquel. Additionally, I had told her my horror stories of what had happened to me regarding medications and she had actually expressed a degree of empathy before Dr. Lantz entered the picture. By now I thought it should be well understood that while I needed to address my insomnia, I also had to be careful.

Aside from our conversation about medication, I had also told Dr. Lantz that I'd contacted a specialist in trauma processing with the hope that perhaps working through some of my childhood memories might lead to better sleep. He was not at all impressed with this idea and suggested strongly that I sign a release of information so that he and Lynn could "tell him all that's going on" with me.

When Lynn called me back, this was something I wanted to talk to her about. Her response was even more discouraging. She simply stated point blank, "You can't have two therapists." There was no, "initiating that must have taken courage," or "I can double check our policies," or even "how can we help you make a transition." It was simply, "you need to choose."

I told Lynn that working with the trauma specialist was important to me, but I would still like to receive symptom management at Cornerstone. She said that was not possible and advised I get Seroquel from a general practitioner in the community. I had done this at a low income clinic once, but there was a lot of doctor turnover there and I was not at all sure a practitioner I had never seen would prescribe it.

When I told her this, she shrugged it off and stated again that it was not ethical for her to treat me if I were to also see the specialist. I didn't understand how trying to get my needs met was only resulting in hostility and indifference from these practitioners. I had already attempted trauma processing with her and it did not go well. I had been doing some on my own, by writing it out, but felt I needed the support of someone with training to help me with the intense feelings it brought up. While I wanted to work with the trauma specialist, I would be paying out of pocket and could barely afford one session per month. He didn't prescribe medication. Still, it was important to me so I informed her that I intended to work with him. That was that. Halfway into my session she let me go.

Journal Entry

September 26, 1999

I have a new job assisting individuals with disabilities. It's a small agency and I am receiving a lot of good training on how to help people live meaningful lives in the community.

This seems like a good fit, but I am struggling nonetheless. At today's meeting I couldn't follow everything. My thinking has really been affected since taking all these medications.

It is hard for me to gain confidence when I can realistically expect my brain to let me down when I am in a meeting. Talking with other people, I don't want to impress anyone, I just want to be competent. I am tired of making a fool of myself.

At my appointment we talked about stress management. Vicki doesn't want any changes of the meds. I am still taking Serzone and Klonopin.

This morning I woke up to the kids snoring in stereo, one laying on each side of me. I can't believe they are already seven and nine. I'm so lucky to be their mom.

FOLLOW THE MONEY

According to Robert Whitaker, an award-winning investigative journalist who has investigated the steady rise of disabling mental illness in both children and adults over the past five decades, in 1903 roughly one out of every 500 people in the United States was hospitalized for mental illness. The drug Thorazine was introduced in 1955, and at that time about one out of every 300 people were disabled by mental disorders. From 1955 to 1987, with the rise of antipsychotic drugs such as Thorazine and Hadol, as well as the older tricyclic antidepressants like Elavil and Anafranil, the number of those disabled by mental illness increased four-fold to about one out of every 75 people being deemed mentally ill.

Around 1988, second-generation psychiatric drugs like Prozac and Paxil (SSRI antidepressants) started hitting the market soon to be followed by the new atypical antipsychotic drugs like Zyprexa, Clozaril and Risperdal. Since the introduction of these drugs, the number of significantly mentally ill persons has continued to rise and now numbers one in every 50 Americans.

Whitaker, who authored the book, *Anatomy of an Epidemic— Magic Bullets, Psychiatric Drugs and the Rise of Mental Illness,* puts it this way, "The number of mentally disabled people in the United States has been increasing at the rate of 150,000 people per year since 1987. That's an increase every day over the last 17 years of 410 people per day newly disabled by mental illness."

This increase has not been offset by pharmaceutical industry expenditures on state-of-the-art psychotrophic medications, which leads one to wonder if the increase could be partly because of it. More is spent on the marketing and promotion of drugs than on their research and development. Tens of thousands of dollars have gone to individual doctors who had in exchange promoted and prescribed these drugs. Many of these doctors are viewed as "thought leaders" in their fields, with other doctors relying upon them for information about new medications and their prescribing.

In the United States in 2000, Prozac sales (Eli Lilly) reached $2.6 billion, Zoloft (Pfizer) reached $1.9 billion, Paxil (Smith Kline Beecham) $1.8 billion, Wellbutrin (Glaxo Smith Kline) $850.9 million, and Effexor (Wyeth - Ayerst) $815.8 million. Combined spending on antipsychotic drugs and antidepressants in the United States jumped from around $500 million in 1986 to nearly $20 billion in 2004.

More is spent on antidepressant medications in the US than the total gross national product of a mid-sized country like Jordan. The amount spent on all psychiatric drugs combined is more than the gross national product of two-thirds of the world's countries. What this adds up to is billions of dollars in increased stock prices, handsome salaries for the managers and owners of pharmaceutical companies, not to mention the perks and kick-backs enjoyed by the psychiatric establishment, medical doctors, researchers, and advertising agencies. In spite of all of this, or perhaps because of it, the mental health of the world's population is deteriorating.

Obviously, the drug companies see it differently. While admitting their products aren't perfect, they hold to the idea that their medications are a life raft for many who are suffering, and until better treatments come along, these drugs should be made widely available. As far as conflicts of interest, pharmaceutical companies see these as merely helpful collaborations

Marcia Angell, a prominent doctor and former editor of the *New England Journal of Medicine*, has repeatedly voiced her concern over conflicts of interest between drug companies and the medical profession. She has expressed concern about industry sponsored science that is embraced by these thought leaders resulting in the widespread prescribing of drugs like SSRI anti-depressants, despite the significant risks they can pose for a large number of patients.

In response to her views, she has been accused of misusing her position to promote an anti-psychiatry and anti-pharmaceutical agenda. In 2012, doctors like John Krystal, president of the American College of Neuropsychopharmacology, expressed indignation about statements Dr. Angell made in an article published in the *New York Review of*

Books in which she talked, (among other things), about problems re-garding the way anti-depressants were being marketed and prescribed.

Dr. Krystal feared her comments would dissuade people from using anti-depressants, impacting those who currently benefit from them as well as those who could benefit from taking them in the fu-ture. "Clinicians face enormous challenges in weighing the risks and benefits of pharmacotherapy with each patient, educating patients about these risks and benefits, and monitoring these risks and benefits on an ongoing basis during treatment," he wrote. He believes that it is dangerous to suggest to the public that these medications don't work, let alone that they could cause harm.

While staunch advocates for pharmaceutical interests like Dr. Krystal profess deep concern for human suffering and a steadfast com-mitment to provide innovative treatments for those who are entrusted to their care, this paternalism abruptly truncates when it comes to those of us who have experienced life-altering adverse effects and recognize them as such. The indignant compassion of those who would protect us from the words of Robert Whittaker and Marcia Angell quickly evaporates when our clinical outcomes manifest the dangers that had been known to them but never disclosed to us. Because physicians are often unaware of the significant dangers regarding many of the drugs they prescribe, when we finally see adverse effects for what they are and resist having them attributed to our own illness, our stories are of-ten discredited while we are slapped with the anti-psychiatry label and discarded into the same waste basket as the doctors who are sounding the alarm.

PART THREE

THE GRIEVANCES

"Revolutions begin when people
who are defined as problems achieve the power
to redefine the problem."

— *John McKnight*

2/17/2014

Disability Rights Ohio
50 West Broad Street Suite 1400
Columbus OH 43215-5923

To whom it may concern:

Enclosed you will find three related Mental Health grievances with additional information. Two of the incidents occurred within minutes of each other and are directly related. The third grievance is due to the repeated barriers I encountered while attempting to obtain information regarding the grievance process.

The systemic nature of the problems I have encountered, along with the fact that I received shockingly inadequate responses from the designated Client Rights Officers in my area, prompted me to bypass the lower levels of the grievance process and to submit these grievances directly to Disability Rights Ohio and the Department of Mental Health and Addiction Services.

I recognize what I submit to you is lengthy. This is not a reflection of any uncontrolled indignation on my part, but of a concern for individuals in the mental health care system, of whom I am one. I would ask that this complaint be seen in that light and not as retaliation toward any individual practitioner, doctor, or staff member.

Sincerely,
Laurie Oakley

First Grievance

RIGHT VIOLATED: *the right to be treated with consideration and respect for personal dignity, autonomy, and privacy.*

On 1/27/14, Dr. Lantz expressed impatience toward me when I decided not to take Trazodone after finding out it could exacerbate my heart arrhythmia. He refused to seriously consider my history of medication sensitivity and neglected to ask basic questions about how I was doing except in connection with taking medication. He was disgusted after I *did* try Trazodone and discontinued because of other side-effects, and he tried to use economic pressure to coerce/punish me saying, "you're gonna have to pay" for lab work to take a tiny dose of Seroquel. He did not respect my rationale for sticking with Seroquel, which is what I have been prescribed for severe insomnia for the past six years. (Note: I did get the lab work he requested).

Right violated: the right to be informed of one's own condition, of proposed or current services, treatment or therapies, and of the alternatives.

With Dr. Lantz there were no alternatives to Trazodone; had I not been informed and aware and able to resist his efforts to control me, I might have continued in the treatment which could have harmed me. He gave me no credit for trying Trazodone, nor any credit for the non-medical approaches I take such as extensive sleep hygiene, caffeine restriction, diet and exercise, supplementation, meditation, yoga, Alanon 12-step program, other stress reducing lifestyle changes, and consulting with a specialist in trauma processing.

> *Right violated: the right to consent to or refuse any service, treatment, or therapy upon full explanation of the expected consequences of such consent or refusal.*

Dr. Lantz never spoke of consequences except for the financial consequences I would incur for switching back to Seroquel. He downplayed heart rhythm side-effects of Trazodone even though I have an arrhythmia. He took me to task for drinking a cup of coffee in the morning saying that it was worse than Trazodone. I was punished for refusing Trazodone even after an honest attempt. When I asked him if he documented that I tried it and experienced side-effects, he said with contempt, "I think you need to leave."

> *Right violated: the right to participate in any appropriate and available agency service, regardless of refusal of one or more other services, treatments, or therapies, or regardless of relapse from earlier treatment in that or another service, unless there is a valid and specific necessity which precludes and/or requires the client's participation in other services. This necessity shall be explained to the client and written in the client's current service plan.*

> *Right violated: the right to be informed in advance of the reason(s) for discontinuance of service provision, and to be involved in planning for the consequences of that event.*

> *Right violated: the right to exercise any and all rights without reprisal in any form including continued and uncompromised access to service.*

104

After learning from Dr. Lantz that his attitude toward me was based upon my self-advocacy in regard to medication sensitivities, I told him we were not a good fit and I needed to see a different psychiatrist. He stated the agency frowned upon clients making such changes and that I should find a provider outside the agency. To me, this communicates a complete lack of respect and disregard for my welfare.

Journal Entry

July 12, 2001

I now have "symptoms." When I went to the ER last month with chest pains they could find nothing. Now the chest pain isn't so bad, but I have numbness, burning, and tingling in my hands and feet. I have no idea what this is. I am not seeking attention by having "symptoms" and I don't mind if people don't acknowledge my "symptoms." I saw Dr. Altman at the residency program where my sister goes and she has ordered some tests. So far she is not passing me off as a nut case.

Physically I don't feel well, but mentally I'm doing okay today. Last night I did have an anxiety attack. My muscles were tight and I couldn't get to sleep. Since the kids' dad died in November I've felt so insecure. Now my fear comes from my "symptoms," and I worry that I, too, could drop dead. I am totally on my own with the kids now. Taking them to his house for visits three days a week at least provided us some structure. Now I don't even want to go out of the house.

I've got to be a better parent. Lately I've just wanted to find the back door, slip out quietly and hide. But I can't afford to just slide by while they're growing up. Their daddy is gone and they're still grieving. Two grieving kids need better from their mom.

Village Behavioral Health

Oakley, Laurie A.
Progress Notes
July 17, 2001
Hour: 10:30
Length: 30
Goal: Medication compliance
Progress: Changing meds around

Client Report of Current Functioning: I stopped the Serzone completely.

Observations of Client: Neatly groomed, tearful.

Topics Covered/Interventions Used/Client Response: Laurie stopped the Serzone on her own because she didn't feel she needed it anymore. However she has increased her somatic complaints and visits to medical doctors. She's concerned about being a hypochondriac. Talked about relationship between stress and body.

Plan: See in 3 months.

Changes to Treatment Plan/Diagnosis: Discontinue Serzone. Continue Klonopin.

Meets Medical Necessity for Continued Treatment Due To: Mood disorder, interpersonal/behavioral difficulties, need to monitor medication, services necessary to maintain current functioning and stabilize gains.

BLACK BOX

The anti-depressant Serzone was approved as safe and put on the market in 1994. In 1999, the FDA required Bristol-Myers, the maker of the drug, to add information to the safety label about the drug causing, "rare reports of liver necrosis and liver failure, in some cases leading to liver transplantation and/or death." Then in early 2001, the FDA told the company to remove the word "rare" from the warning. Almost one year later, the FDA required Bristol-Myers to put a "black box" warning on the label, the visibility of which was intended to alert doctors and the public to Serzone's liver toxicity. By 2004, the drug had been taken off the market.

I was prescribed Serzone in 1998 and took it well into 2001. No one brought to my attention that serious liver damage had been associated with the drug. Obviously, at some point it was included in the information provided by the pharmacy, but like most people, I only read it once or twice, and quickly at that. Like most people, I trusted the doctors in charge of my care, and since they had no concerns, I didn't have any either.

After taking a look at how new medications make it onto the market, the thought of physicians prescribing them brings to mind the scene from the movie Fantasia where Micky Mouse puts on the sorcerer's hat and directs a broom to carry buckets of water for him. It's all fun and games until he can't make the broom stop, things get out of hand, and it becomes evident he knows very little about what he is doing. This isn't so much a judgment of doctors but of the fact that, without knowing it, they are often acting on what they don't realize is biased drug industry information.

According to Dr. Howard Brody, author of the book, *Hooked: Ethics, The Medical Profession, and the Pharmaceutical Industry*, drug companies too often turn a blind eye to the dangers of a drug in order to quickly get it into the hands of doctors who can prescribe it. Most doctors believe that when a medication makes it onto the market, it is backed by solid research proving its safety and efficacy.

Additionally, doctors simply don't have the time to thoroughly investigate the research on the multiple products made available to them. Because industry has so much control over the science that ultimately gets their drugs approved, and because they have bought their way into academia as well as the medical journals that doctors rely on, many who prescribe drug treatments are completely unaware of the dangers many medications pose to their patients.

On Dr. Brody's blog, he tells of the case of Pradaxa, an anti-clotting medication approved in 2010 for people with irregular heartbeat. At least 1000 deaths have been attributed to the drug so far, deaths that can be linked to drug company profit motive.

Pradaxa is made by the German firm Boehringer Ingelheim, and was intended to be superior to Warfarin, an anti-clotting medication that requires several blood tests to make sure it is working correctly. Pradaxa was considered superior to Warfarin on the basis of being an anti-clotting medication that did not require those tests.

One of the risks with Warfarin is that a patient's bleeding can become uncontrollable, the antidote for which is to give a dose of vitamin K intravenously. Pradaxa works differently and initially there was no antidote for persons who experienced profuse bleeding while taking the drug. During research studies, a pharmaceutical company scientist noted this and concluded that blood tests might be necessary for at least some patients to avoid this dangerous reaction.

Because the company wanted to show Pradaxa was superior to Warfarin in order to get it approved, and avoiding a need for tests was the way they had planned to do this, several scientists and other company officials collectively decided against publishing this conclusion. The drug was approved on that basis while Boehringer Ingelheim kept the lid on information that could have prevented the needless deaths. By the time patients began suing the drug firm, it had made over two billion dollars from the sale of this medication.

For a pharmaceutical company, lawsuits like this are just a cost of doing business. Far from being deterred by the prospect of legal actions, these companies simply factor the costs into their astronomical budgets. Drug companies have such large profits that often they are able to drag out court proceedings until the plaintiff's funds dry up, even when those plaintiffs are governmental entities acting on behalf of injured citizens. By the time a new drug's dangerous effects become apparent, these corporations have long since lined their pockets with blood soaked cash.

With this in mind it can be argued that when it comes to pharmaceuticals, there is no such thing as informed consent, the process by which a patient agrees to a treatment only after receiving all available information about the benefits and significant risks as well as other available options. It's a hard pill to swallow that pharmaceutical companies have so much influence in drug testing, approval, and medical education, while doctors who trust and rely on this information don't have a clue.

Zyprexa is a psychiatric drug with a similar history and is one of the many medications I was given with assurances it was safe only to learn much later that it had significant risks like diabetes. Dr. Mark Ragins, a leading psychiatrist in the mental health recovery movement, stated in 2010, "For me the last straw with drug companies was when I found out that they knew about diabetes and Zyprexa all along and intentionally hid it from doctors, leading us to put people at risk without knowing it."

The list of drugs that get approval before significant risks come to light is long and no doubt includes many medications that are still on the market. Thankfully, Serzone was finally taken off. I can't say I was hurt by Serzone, but I do know I stopped taking it after noticing chronic, urinary side-effects. I also lost a significant amount of weight as a result of taking the drug which is a symptom of liver toxicity. I took it for almost three years and yet couldn't tell you if it worked or not. For me, what worked was anything that didn't cause panic attacks. By that time, I don't remember being depressed so much as being "mentally ill." Symptoms caused by drugs that had been marketed deceptively had made me a part of their system.

Meanwhile, my identity was being skewed with psychiatric labels that buried any possibility of the medication side-effects ever being diagnosed. I was continually anxious and unsettled while on these drugs and spent years clinging to their care in a manner not unlike what they would label Stockholm Syndrome. And when I was finally able to do something so bold as to quit taking Serzone, then *I* became the problem.

Second Grievance

RIGHT VIOLATED: *the right to be treated with consideration and respect for personal dignity, autonomy, and privacy.*

Right violated: the right to have the opportunity to consult with independent treatment specialists or legal counsel, at one's own expense.

Right violated: the right to be informed in advance of the reason(s) for discontinuance of service provision, and to be involved in planning for the consequences of that event.

Right violated: the right to exercise any and all rights without reprisal in any form including continued and un-compromised access to service.

1//27/14 With my therapist, Lynn Merek, when I related what had happened with Dr. Lantz, instead of being informed of my right to the grievance process, she asked why I want to see the doctor if I won't take medication. I reminded her that I take Seroquel. I told her that I was consulting with a specialist to begin trauma processing, and instead of expressing interest in how this might benefit me, she immediately said I could not have two therapists. I stated I desired to continue my monthly appointments for symptom management at Cornerstone, but she said I would need to choose between her and the trauma specialist. I told her that left me without access to symptom management and Seroquel. She suggested I ask a general practitioner in the community. I told her I had done this before and would need to check into it again, and that consulting with the specialist was important to me. She let me go half an hour early without offering to schedule another appointment, presumably with the understanding I would no longer be receiving services. Again, this demonstrates a complete lack of regard for my welfare.

2/14/14 I received, in a Cornerstone identified envelope (a privacy violation), a letter from Lynn stating that my case with Cornerstone was closed. She said this action was taken because the agency had not heard from me in the two weeks since my last appointment. She stated that they assumed I was getting therapy services with someone else and that I was getting medication from a primary care provider. I was not yet established with either of those services and would still prefer to have my psychotropic medication prescribed and monitored by a psychiatrist.

Journal Entry

August 1, 2001

The kids' dad has been gone eight months. They seem to be doing okay. This fall I will start working at their school. My first and most important job is to be here for them. I hope we can eat out a little less and spend more quality time together.

I am still having these "symptoms," of what I am not sure. I was able to stop taking Serzone, but I'm not sleeping at all when I stop taking Klonopin, and it seems like my "symptoms" get worse. At my mental health appointment, Vicki reminded me of the relationship between stress and the body, and encouraged me to take my meds. I told her I am aware that this may be all in my head, but the symptoms are very physical.

The Henri Nowen meditation for today says that we should not feel guilty for being who we are or for being "where we are." Still, I want to take some steps to get out of this rut. Whatever it takes.

TOLERANCE WITHDRAWAL

There came a point in all of this when I recognized that since I didn't have the major problems I'd had after I was first medicated for depression, it probably wouldn't be a bad idea to return to a life in which I wasn't so dependent upon doctors and drugs. While this sounded good in theory, I had no idea with what and with whom I was dealing.

I had been on Klonopin for four years by the time tolerance withdrawal symptoms developed, and I was unknowingly and thoroughly dependent. Not only did I not know just how chained I was to this medication and to the system that was doling it out, I had no inkling the symptoms I was experiencing were a direct result of having developed an iatrogenic dependence to my prescribed medicine.

According to Professor Ashton, who devoted her life to researching psychoactive drugs and who operated a benzodiazepine withdrawal clinic in the UK from 1982 to 1994, tolerance withdrawal is different for different people. But sooner or later, if you're taking a benzodiazepine on a regular basis without increasing the dose, your brain will make compensations to work around it. What is interesting is that, not only do the drugs lose effectiveness, they can also cause an increase in anxiety, a worsening of insomnia, and multiple other symptoms that the individual did not have before starting the drug. Doctors generally misdiagnose the tolerance withdrawal symptoms of persons prescribed benzodiazepines as a worsening mental or physical condition. Then the dose might be increased, often with other drugs being prescribed as well. This might temporarily fix the problem but obviously there are good reasons to avoid this.

Speaking only for myself, when I was first given Klonopin to treat panic attacks caused by SSRI anti-depressants, it worked so well that I developed a strong psychological need for it. Added to that was the fact that it was the only medication I felt a positive result from when the others seemed to be causing major trouble. Looking back,

116

Klonopin was probably to blame for the mental fog, memory loss, and cognitive impairment I had attributed to anti-depressants.

Aside from a possible placebo effect in light of my psychological dependency, the drug was likely not doing me much good after the first month or two, and probably had something to do with the suicidal depression I ended up experiencing. I simply kept taking it because my doctors kept prescribing it and because it was the only thing that I felt had worked.

Four years into treatment with Klonopin when I began experiencing tolerance withdrawal, I had unusual sensations as well as pain in many areas of my body, tense and tight muscles, weakness in my hands and wrists, increased anxiety, and a phenomenon called formication. Formication is an unnerving skin sensation that often leads a person to believe there are bugs crawling on them. It is a classic withdrawal symptom. I would experience this just as I was trying to fall asleep and would reawaken repeatedly. Another symptom I had was hypersensitivity to stimuli such as light and sound. Buttons clinking inside the dryer several rooms away caused me to startle while trying to fall asleep. It was at this point that I began developing chronic insomnia.

These were only my symptoms. Others have many symptoms I never had such as gastrointestinal issues, tinnitus, difficulties of coordination, vision problems, muscle twitches and tics, agoraphobia, a metallic taste in the mouth, dry cough, loss of appetite, among many others.

This often unrecognized condition in persons taking benzodiazepines is anything but unusual. Doctors see it every day and routinely attribute it to other causes, never realizing it is tolerance withdrawal to a medicine listed right there in the chart. This is standard practice which I can only guess was established in the first years these drugs were made available. Doctors, by and large, rely upon "thought leaders" in their profession and practice what they observe other doctors practicing. Because benzodiazepines have been around for over fifty years, most assume there is nothing new to learn about them.

From the beginning, benzodiazepines were deemed "safe" drugs only because they did not cause the respiratory depression that led to death like the older barbiturates had. It's harder to deny the effects of drugs that outright kill you. The adverse effects of benzodiazepines would be subtler, many not showing up until much later. Meanwhile, as the very first blockbuster drugs, they were a gateway to addicting profits for the pharmaceutical industry. Never before had any drug come close to bringing in the tantalizing profits that the benzodiazepines did. Doctors became habituated to this class of medications as well, as they were powerful treatments making their patients feel significantly better right away. By the time some doctors began recognizing major problems with this class of drugs, *everyone* was hooked.

The dominant feature of addiction is denial. For a pharmaceutical company to acknowledge the many adverse effects of benzodiazepines would mean their drug (astronomical profits) would be significantly cut. For doctors to acknowledge such might mean not only giving up the power of prescribing a highly effective drug to more patients than necessary, but to admit that many of the prescriptions already written had caused significant harm.

By avoiding these hard truths, those who were benefiting the most from this class of drugs, the pharmaceutical companies along with doctors, ended up scapegoating patients who had developed true addiction. The behavior of drug-seeking addicts was made the focus which served to deflect from the need for further research. By writing off as somatization the "vague" symptoms of anxious patients as well as treating these symptoms as separate conditions, the whole system deluded itself to maintain its dependency upon benzodiazepines.

The path of drug abuse is never sustainable and those suffering from addiction usually end up hurting a lot of people in order to get their fix. The corporate pharmaceutical complex is continually on the lookout for new chemical combinations to patent for large markets in order to maintain their supply of astronomical profits. Considering the wretched history of benzodiazepines, one might find it unthinkable that these corporations are now looking to market, (perhaps a new version of), a benzodiazepine to individuals already struggling with the condition of autism. If there was ever a time for an intervention, this just might be it.

16

Third Grievance

RIGHT VIOLATED: *the right to be treated with consideration and respect for personal dignity, autonomy, and privacy.*

Right violated: the right to have oral and written instructions for filing a grievance.

Right violated: the right to be fully informed of all rights.

Each agency shall make provision for posting the grievance procedure in a conspicuous place and for distributing a copy of the written grievance procedure to each applicant and each client, upon request.

Written grievance procedure shall include the name, title, location, hours of availability, and telephone number of the client rights officer with a statement of that person's responsibility to accept and oversee the process of any grievance filed by a client or other person or agency on behalf of a client; and assurance that staff will explain any and all aspects of client rights and the grievance procedure upon request.

1/27/14 I asked the receptionist for information on filing a grievance and was handed a blank appointment card with Rose Jamison's name, titles, and agency phone number on the back. If the grievance procedure is posted, I was not informed of it.

1/29/14 Rose returned my call within 24 hours. I told her I wanted to file a grievance and she asked how my rights had been violated. I gave her a quick summary of two instances. Instead of giving me the information I was requesting, she stated that in one of the instances my rights had not been violated. She asked if I wanted to continue getting treatment with the doctor I was filing a grievance about, and also asked if I wanted to receive treatment at a different location. I repeated that I wanted her to send me the proper paperwork. She told me that protocol was for her to fill out the grievance forms and then I would sign it. I told her I would be willing to meet with her but for now I only wanted information. She asked me again about what rights I thought were violated. I told her I had a pretty good idea of what rights had been and were being violated. At this point she asked for my address.

1/31/14 In a Cornerstone identified envelope (a violation of privacy), I received Attachment I: Staff Guidelines for Service Site Procedure (for agency staff); numbers 15-25 of the Client Rights, (1-14 missing); and two Attachment E: Cornerstone Grievance Forms. The cover letter summarized what was sent and no other information was given.

2/11/14 Called Maggie Kramer, CRO (Client Rights Officer), for Hamilton County Mental Health Services Board, and left a message saying I wanted to file a grievance and needed the information on how to go about it. She quickly returned my call. I told her Rose had sent partial information. She said the next step was to meet with Rose and who would give me instructions on how to fill out the grievances. Then she said while she would also be happy to help me, the next step up from Rose is CRO Janette Williamson.

2/13/14 After calling Janette Williamson and leaving a message, her assistant, Leslie Simon, returned my call. I told her what I had received from Rose and said I didn't think that was all of the information I was requesting. She took down my name and address and said she would send what I needed. She wanted to help me determine over the phone what right had been denied, so I told her my primary complaint. She then said Rose had sent the right forms, explained a bit about how to fill them out, and told me to send them to her. She said she would follow up with staff at Cornerstone. She did not send anything.

Meanwhile, I spent a considerable amount of time searching the internet for the information I had requested in order to know what my rights are, how to go about filing a grievance, who I can submit the grievance to, and what I can expect to have happen after I file. I can't imagine how someone with more severe limitations might have accomplished this.

Journal Entry

September 9, 2001

Dr Altman has left the residency program so I switched to the group at General Family Practice. I hope I can continue to see this doctor because he took my symptoms seriously. It was embarrassing but I had to tell him I think we might have some kind of bugs in our house. At night I can feel them crawling on me. I think it may be a type of mite because I can't see anything. This has been a more trying experience than I ever could have imagined and I feel so uncomfortable in my own home. I've been doing laundry like crazy. All I can think about is getting rid of this so we can get back to normal. Socially it's embarrassing. People whom I've told won't set foot here and I don't blame them.

I am irritable and depressed. I am not sleeping well, but I refuse to take more psych meds. I am completely off Serzone and only take half a milligram of Klonopin at night now.

The doctor is doing some lab work to determine if the pain and tingling in my hands and feet is due to something called Raynaud's. He also thought it may be some kind of allergic reaction and prescribed some stuff.

I am a mess from this. I feel like I literally need time to heal from this. This bug problem added to my "mysterious illness" is completely overwhelming me.

General Family Practice

Oakley, Laurie A.
Progress Notes
September 11, 2001

S: 36-year-old white female reports bodily aches and burning sensation in hands and feet, minimal now. States that she is often told her symptoms are related to her anxiety disorder and requests that we rule out any other problem. States there may be a mite problem in her house which causes her to "itch all over." She has occasionally broken out in a papular rash and on two different occasions even had some mid chest tightness and aching, especially with exertion. She has called an exterminator who has collected samples to find out if there are mites in the home. Currently she is staying outside of the house. She has been having some problems with Raynaud's phenomenon in her hands on and off for some time now. This has been worse since the papular rash, with occasional chest tightness and shortness of breath having occurred with the mite infestation. She denies fever, chills, or sweats. No nausea or vomiting. No vertigo.

Current Medications: 0.5 mg Klonopin daily.

O: Patient is alert and in no acute distress. Lungs are clear. Heart regular. There is purplish discoloration of the distal tips of all of her fingers which are cool to the touch. Currently they are not painful.

A: 1. Allergies—unknown if this could be secondary to recent dust mites in her house.
   2. Raynaud's phenomenon—unknown if this is an associated immune response.

3. Hypersensitive reaction—left shoulder—suspected bug bite healing.

P: Allegra 180 mg daily. Albuterol MDI—two puffs as needed for chest tightness or shortness of breath. kenalog cream 0.1% applied to the affected area as needed for itching, two weeks maximum. Apparently this patient has already been evaluated for specific causes of her Raynaud's phenomenon, including blood work and ANA, sed rate, CBC, etc. She asked many questions about this today, all of which were answered for her. Reassured patient that although she has symptoms of psychiatric illness this does not mean her symptoms will be disregarded. Patient agreed with current plan. It should be noted that the patient's left wrist was also examined secondary to complaints of some pain in this area without any abnormalities being noted today.

17

Related Incident

THE FOLLOWING MEDICAL RECORD illustrates how the grievances I am filing cannot be understood or sufficiently addressed without looking at larger systemic problems. As you read this, keep in mind that in most cases the drug in question, Klonopin, should not be prescribed for more than 2 - 4 weeks. Physiological dependency can begin in as little as two weeks.

When I first spoke with Dr. McDonnell, (at Cornerstone in 2007), I explained my history of medication sensitivity in regard to SSRIs and the symptoms of those drug reactions being treated with Klonopin. I told her that the practitioner who prescribed Klonopin for daily use, long-term assured me I could not become addicted or dependent on such a low dose. I also told Dr. McDonnell that I had been prescribed what is considered a low dose of that drug for over a period of eight years. The last four of those years I experienced symptoms of tolerance withdrawal that were misdiagnosed by at least half a dozen doctors as hypochondria. These practitioners all told me the same thing: take your medicine. Because I had learned to be cautious in regard to medications, I did not comply with taking all of the drugs I was prescribed over that four year period to treat the symptoms of undiagnosed tolerance withdrawal. When I was finally able to stop taking Klonopin in 2004 on my own, I experienced withdrawal. It was then that I realized I had been in tolerance withdrawal for at least four years. After I got through withdrawal, the "hypochondria" symptoms lessened, leaving me with only one unmanageable problem: insomnia. (I did not have insomnia before being put on all of these medications).

Dr. McDonnell's response to this, aside from what she wrote in this medical record, was to tell me what a problem clients who are seeking Klonopin are, and that she wished I could talk some sense into them. She also conveyed the attitude that my past experiences were due, not to systemic problems in healthcare, but simply to a few practitioners who had made mistakes.

As for what she wrote in my record: although I clearly reported to Dr. McDonnell that the Klonopin I took was prescribed, that I usually took less than what was prescribed, and that I refused to ever take more than 1.5 mg, she recorded my former use of Klonopin in the illicit substance use category.

This is no small mistake. Not only is this an absolute denial of responsibility to respond to a client's report of a widespread systemic failure to recognize the predictable occurrence of tolerance withdrawal in a patient misprescribed a small dose of Klonopin over the course of several years, it is denied in such a way to place blame and further stigmatization upon the person who is reporting grave errors and abuses.

Journal Entry

September 27, 2001

I think I am sick, as in illness or disease. This doctor thinks it may be Raynaud's syndrome or something called peripheral neuropathy, and has started me on new medic-

Maybe I need treatment for depression, but the side effects of new psych meds would confuse me with what's already going on. The only way I can describe this is to say I have pain, and it feels like it's in my veins if that is even possible. And I still have chest pain. I am so concerned with getting a diagnosis. I don't want it to be anything but I need to know what this is. The last thing I want to be told

I am tired as hell. Nothing is comfortable right now. This is my favorite time of year and I feel too overwhelmed to

I am walking every day and trying to eat right. Whether or not I have an illness, I do have serious depression. I need to take care of myself.

127

General Family Practice

Oakley, Laurie A.
Progress Notes
September 20, 2001

S: 36-year-old female returns complaining of increased pain and achiness in her hands and wrists bilaterally as well as muscular pain in all of her extremities. Reports tingling and pain in her extremities which is not contained in the muscles or the joints. This occurs irregardless of activity or rest. Symptoms seem to be getting worse since she was last seen here on September 11, 2001. Since June, she has also been having dull aches in the mid portion of her chest with symptoms worse at night, regardless of whether she is lying down or not. In June, she also went to the emergency room with this chest pain and had a negative cardiac workup. She has never had a chest x-ray, although she had significant blood work done at Heartland Medicine Residency in July to rule out autoimmune causes of her symptoms. The inhaler she received has not helped her symptoms. The papular rash she had previously is no longer bothering her since taking the Allegra. She denies fever, chills or sweats. No shortness of breath or cough.

Current Medications: Klonopin 1 mg daily, Allegra 180 mg daily, Albuterol MDI as needed, kenalog cream 0.1%.

O: Patient is alert and in no acute distress. Lungs are clear, heart is regular.

A: Raynaud's phenomenon—without much in the way

of objective evidence for this today, although patient complains her pain is worse. Chest pain.

P: Try Voltaren XL 100 mg—one daily for one week. Take one aspirin 325 mg daily. Obtain chest x-ray. Waiting on old records from the Heartland Residency so we can review these and plan further workup without duplication of previous tests. Return in one week or as needed.

18

Further Declarations

I HAVE THE RIGHT FOR my well-documented history of medication sensitivities to be acknowledged and believed.

I have a right to be believed in the present when reporting major side-effects (on both SSRIs and Klonopin) that occurred in the past when I was too incapacitated by them to recognize them as such.

I have the right for my doctor to take into consideration my report of those side-effects being not recognized as side-effects but diagnosed as a deterioration of my own mental health by the doctors I was being treated by at the time.

I have a right for the physical and psychological harm I received within mental health and medical care systems to be acknowledged and for its seriousness to be addressed, as my medical record indicates that this did, in fact, occur.

I have a right to have access to a doctor who has the time and interest to become at least minimally invested in the process with me, who is interested in knowing me and is sensitive to my particular situation.

I have a right to participate in a partnership with those who are treating my condition.

I have the right to exercise caution in light of my well-known and thoroughly documented medication sensitivities without being subject to disgust by my doctor.

I have a right to be proactive and to advocate for myself with my doctor, especially when a proposed treatment reflects his failure to fully consider my medical history.

I have the right to question treatments proposed by my doctor and to be treated with respect even when those questions make my doctor uncomfortable.

I have the right to a referral if my doctor outwardly or inwardly does not believe in or respect me.

I have a right not to be told to leave in a demeaning manner after advocating for myself with my doctor.

I have a right to not be intimidated by my doctor.

As a childhood trauma survivor, I have a right to not be revictimized in a system that is intended to help me recover from abuse.

Likewise, I have the right to not be scapegoated in a system that was founded on the intention of helping people like me.

I have a right not to be prejudged by a practitioner or doctor who has not taken the time to review and consider my documented history of abuse.

I have a right not to be subjected to the complete passive witness of current providers when reporting harm resulting from systemic practices in community mental health systems when those systemic practices are still in place.

I have a right to assistance from professionals who recognize my healing as my own process.

I have the right to educate myself about my condition and possible treatments and to act on that knowledge without reprisal.

I have a right to be treated by professionals who recognize that I know a great deal about my own situation and who acknowledge and value all my efforts to recover, past and present.

I have the right for my practitioners to recognize all of my efforts, past and present, before making negative judgments about me.

I have the right to exercise self-respect in regard to how things are going with a practitioner and to adjust the way I approach my therapy when that practitioner's attitudes toward me become chronically unhelpful.

I have a right to pull back from therapy with a practitioner whose primary technique is to constantly challenge my way of thinking without also recognizing my strengths and encouraging me to build upon them.

I have the right to work with a practitioner who takes some responsibility for the therapy process and helps me to stay on track with my goals instead of supporting my psychiatrist's goal to disempower me.

I have the right to work with practitioners who base their treatment of me upon their own relationship with me and not on another practitioner's opinion of me, especially if that opinion is unfavorable.

I have the right not to be discriminated against on the basis of being intelligent and informed, especially when the very nature of my illness has made advocating for myself nearly impossible.

I have a right not to be discriminated against because I "look too good" or function highly in spite of severe discomfort.

In case this is an issue:

I have a right to have thoughts of filing for Social Security disability and to voice those thoughts to the therapist who is treating me for severe, chronic insomnia. (I first brought it up in 2007 and as of yet I have not filed).

I have a right to at least consider petitioning for the disability benefits that I might be eligible for based on work I performed in the 20 years before and 10 years since I began struggling with severe, chronic insomnia, without being given the boot by my practitioners.

In regard to systemic issues:

133

In light of the scientific information that has been made available by Dr. Malcolm Lader, Dr. Heather Ashton, and others, I have the right for my practitioners to *at least consider* that my insomnia could be a residual effect from having been prescribed Klonopin for eight years. No one can know for sure, but that possibility should be acknowledged by community mental health care systems who at one time added medication compliance to their goals for me because *they* thought I needed years of therapy with the dangerous drug Klonopin.

I have the right to receive treatment from practitioners who are at least minimally aware of the controversy related to pharmaceutical influence within medicine who can be open-minded while reviewing my medical records in light of that controversy.

I have a right to be treated within a system that will take responsibility for its own systemic practices, past and present and in all locations, and not place blame on individual practitioners (or clients), for problems that resulted from those systemic practices.

Journal Entry

October 17, 2001

I met with the Rheumatologist today. I told him about the pain and tingling in my hands and feet as well as the pain in my chest. I asked him if this could be in any way connected to the mites we may have had in our house, but he doesn't think there is a connection. He doesn't think it is an allergic reaction or Raynaud's and he said my previous labs looked fine. I told him I was highly sensitive to medications, especially antidepressants. He told me not to worry and that I don't have any true drug allergies. He said that my symptoms were unusual and nothing that he had ever connected with any disease. I got the sense that he views me as one of those women who go to the doctor seeking attention. He said he will do blood work but it is likely everything will come back negative.

I am in an incredibly bad mood and depressed. Not sad, just down, tired. I have some kind of medical problem and really need to know what it is.

What else can I do except focus on what I can do to take care of myself and the kids. They are enjoying school. Grace has made a good connection with Gwen, the art therapist I have been taking her to since her daddy died. Although Marley isn't interested in the art therapy, I've started him in karate classes. He really enjoys karate, has made some friends, and seems to be making a connection with the teacher. I can't wait until our lives become comfortable again.

Holcolm Rheumatology Clinic

Oakley, Laurie A.
Rheumatology Consultation
October 17, 2001
Problem: Hand pain, positive ANA

.

History of Present Illness: The patient is a 36-year-old patient of General Family Practice. She gives a fairly vague
and somewhat unusual history of intermittent pain in the
hands and fullness in the chest.

Initially when she had the fullness in the chest she was
seen in the emergency room where she had a normal EKG
and chest x-ray. This was several months ago.

Since that time she has had intermittent fleeting discomfort
in the chest without shortness of breath. It is more of an
"aching" going across the front anterior chest but not radi-
ating down the arms, into the jaw or into the back.

The pain in her hands is not in the joints. It is not in the
muscles. She has no dysesthesias or stinging with it. She
says her pain is in the "veins" and says they sometimes
look "purplish."

She also wonders about "mites" in her house. She says that
she has had small "bites" as well as itching. I asked her
who told her that the house has mites, and she says that it
is no one. The exterminators were unable to actually find
anything in her house causing these "bites." She has used
various chemicals on her own without direction of the exterminators to try to get rid of them, but she says that the
symptoms which she now has predates the use of the
chemicals she was using.

136

No actual Raynaud's phenomenon is described. She does not give triphasic color change reports. She has had no fever, chills, or sweats or any red, hot, or swollen joints.

She has a written description of her symptoms and this is included in her chart. She says that she has a "weakness" in the hands while doing everyday work. She says she feels like she is over-extending herself.

Her chest pain episodes began in June, and they have been intermittent since that time.

She reports that the palms and the sides of her feet itch and then turn red. The itching then turns into aching.

Her laboratory testing has shown a normal sedimentation rate and an essentially negative ANA. She had an unremarkable CBC. There is a past normal TSH and negative rheumatoid factor.

Past Medical History: Anemia
        Medications:
           1. Klonopin 1 mg bedtime
           2. Aspirin 1 each morning
           3. Allegra
           4. Cyclobenzaprine
           5. Ibuprofen

Allergies: She has no true drug allergies, however, she is "highly sensitive to some medications" especially anti-depressants.

Family History: Patient has no family history of inflammatory arthritis or connective tissue disease.

Social History: Patient reports no alcohol or tobacco use.

Review of Systems: Positive for irregular heart beat, sleeping poorly, tingling in the hands and feet and being colder than others.

Physical Examination: Patient is in no apparent distress. I see absolutely no skin abnormality, no color change apparent in the hands. Range of motion of all peripheral joints is normal. She has trigger points on examination today.

Impression:
1. Hand pain with vague discoloration of uncertain etiology. This does not fit a diagnosis for Raynaud's phenomenon. I am not certain what is going on here.
2. Vague chest fullness. It sounds noncardiac, but I am uncertain of the etiology for this.
3. Essentially negative ANA at 1:40. General Family Practice laboratory calls this positive. I think that this is almost certainly of doubtful clinical significance. I do not think that this is related to her symptoms as above.

We will check anti-Smith, Ro/La, RNP, and a double-stranded DNA, but I think it is likely that they will all be negative.

Her symptoms are vague, and I see nothing on physical examination. I am not certain what is going on with the patient. I told her that any potential test at this time would be somewhat of a long shot given the fact that her symptoms and signs are not pathognomonic for any condition of which I am aware.
At times patients with skin changes as described above may have livido reticularis. Because of this possibility, we will check cryo and hepatitas C. We will also check antiphospholipid antibodies and lupus anticoagulant.

I did tell the patient that her symptoms are unusual and that this was nothing which I had seen or heard before, and they are not indicative of any serious condition of which I am aware. This does bring up the possibility of a factitious or psychosocial relationship to some of her symptoms.

The bottom line is that I told the patient I am not sure what is going on here. I do not believe that this is lupus or any other connective tissue disease. I do not believe that it is likely to be a rheumatic disease either.

Unfortunately, her symptoms do not sound muscular, and they do not sound neuropathic, and I would not even know what other system to investigate if the above testing is negative.

19

Final Thoughts

OBVIOUSLY I BELIEVE WHAT I experienced within this particular agency and with these individual practitioners is a symptom of a much larger problem. Because I link these incidences
to what I have already experienced, both in Kansas and Ohio, it is my
belief that the system to investigate would be the relationship between
the Community Mental Health Systems and the profit driven Pharmaceutical Companies. Any action that stops short of a thorough look at
how these corporations influence treatment decisions and pharmaceutical prescribing is inadequate.

I recognize that these grievances have very little influence in
the face of the millions of dollars pharmaceutical companies spend in
order to secure their domination of healthcare. I recognize that most
individuals will not be able to wrap their heads around this problem,
and that by the very nature of one's involvement of having a livelihood
enmeshed with pharmaceutical interests, some people cannot afford to.
Still, these things need to be said.

I am not implying that all medications are bad, but that the
over-marketing of pharmaceuticals as well as pharmaceutical company
influence in physician education and government lobbying for the sake
of corporate profit, are adversely affecting the lives of, and even leading to an untimely death for, many clients and patients. Until informed
consent is truly informed, for a decent human being there are really

only two choices: remove yourself from the situation or join those who are working on solutions.

Until names like Malcolm Lader and Heather Ashton are as well-known and respected by Community Health Agency doctors as Pfizer and Astra Zeneca currently are; until revelations from people like Robert Whitaker and Peter Breggin are as welcome in these centers as Eli Lilly drug reps, samples, and other freebies are; until the information Howard Brody, David Healey, and Marcia Angell make available to doctors about pharmaceutical company influence in the continuing education of doctors and medical journals is given the weight that the biased industry funded science is; until those prescribing medications carefully consider what groups like the Maine Benzodiazepine Study Group are telling us about their own findings on the short and long-term effects of several classes of drugs; until these things come to pass, no Community Mental Health Center in this country is a safe place for any citizen to put his or her trust.

I am not unaware of the complete unlikelihood that I would survive what I have and make it back to tell the story. I could have dropped off the map in 1997 when I was extremely suicidal after taking anti-depressants. Many on these medications do, with suicide being attributed to their depression. I could have remained lost in the mental fog of the multiple medications. Many are, and have it attributed to their mental illness for which they are prescribed more drugs. I could have developed secondary drug addictions while attempting to self-medicate the effects of prescribed drugs. Many do and are tragically stigmatized for becoming chemically dependent; many die from dangerous drug combinations and fatal overdoses. I could have succumbed to some of the more serious side-effects of these drugs, like liver failure caused by Serzone. Many do, and these deaths are very rarely investigated or reported as being possibly related to medications the person was taking.

As a personal care assistant, I have seen developmentally disabled individuals take multiple medications daily for their entire lifetimes. I assisted a woman whose large pill box was so full that she had to buy a second one. She walked out of her doctor's office with a new drug on a Friday and was dead by the following Monday. No one even thought to question whether or not medications had anything to do with the death of this woman who was in her late forties. I was later assigned to assist a man to see his doctor when his evening staff were having difficulty getting him to go to bed at night. I questioned the doctor whose solution was to give him a long-term benzodiazepine prescription. She let me know on no uncertain terms that there are experts on these matters and I wasn't one of them. I have accompanied individuals to medical appointments in which almost the entire visit was spent focused on the multiple medications the person is taking, with no focus whatsoever on nutrition or lifestyle. I have been involved in the care of developmentally disabled children who have been started on long-term treatments with psychotropic medications in the very first years of their lives. I have struggled with the ethics of supporting individuals whose needs required me to administer a whole plethora of medications daily which no one has tested together or could reasonably know just what effects they might be having both short and long-term. Even in a simple case, practitioners miss things. I was given the antibiotic, Cipro, which can interact with the one medication I do take: Seroquel. Neither the prescribing doctor nor the pharmacist told me this. I had to do my homework.

With this in mind, I cannot imagine what it would be like to be in the criminal justice system where non-compliance to taking prescribed medications impacts one's very treatment within the justice system and even one's right to become free in society, or for individuals locked in psychiatric hospitals where the primary treatments involve a whole host of pharmaceuticals. I can't imagine what it is like for children who have medication compliance as a requisite for school attendance, or for those in foster care who have powerful atypical antipsychotics and other medications given to them that have effects not only on a developing brain but on the very length of one's life. I cannot imagine what it is like for elderly patients and their families when drugs like benzodiazepines contribute to serious incidents like falls, auto accidents, and tragic conditions like dementia, and when anti-psychotics are prescribed that lead to early death. I can't imagine the impact medications have on the lives of toddlers who are being prescribed powerful drugs for ADHD at tender ages when healthy brain development is so crucial.

Therefore, in filing these grievances, I am not only petitioning for myself, but for any and all who are lost in these systems for lack of information, knowledge, or means of understanding or addressing what is happening to them, and for those who find it impossible, or nearly impossible, to advocate for themselves.

WAKE UP

Like most people, I remember where I was on September 11, 2001. While my kids were at school I was fleeing our "bug infested" mobile home, checking into a cheap motel nearby. The desk clerk's eyes were transfixed upon a small portable TV. I asked her what was happening and she replied, "They got us!"

I spent most of that day fumigating our home and going to doctors appointments before picking my kids up from school. I took them to our ratty motel room where they watched Cartoon Network and ate Burger King kids' meals while I carefully removed my clothes and put them in trash bags (in case there were bugs), before hopping into a hot bath.

Later, I joined them as they watched TV and we flipped through all the cable channels. Several stations were airing coverage of the attack and we paused for a moment on one showing large plumes of smoke billowing from the burning towers as victims jumped from the windows. We quickly flipped it back to cartoons.

To tell the truth, I didn't have the capacity to recognize the full magnitude of what had happened to those innocent victims on that September day. On top of my own anxious preoccupation with the symptoms of tolerance withdrawal and my visits to doctors who were nowhere near diagnosing it, the kids and I were still living in the aftershock of our own loss.

Wayne's situation, I would later learn, looked suspiciously like a Vioxx death. It occurred around the same time that Vioxx, a multi-billion-dollar drug that ended up being the focus of the biggest drug recall disaster in the history of western medicine, was being aggressively marketed by the drug company, Merck, and was being widely prescribed as a safer option for pain relief than over-the-counter medicines like ibuprofen and acetaminophen. Vioxx was said to be easier on the gastrointestinal tract. This was a year before the terrorist attacks, and also around the time Wayne had been desperately trying to get relief for his chronically aching feet.

Vioxx was approved by the FDA in May of 1999. Many small studies had been done and while a possible heart risk was noted, not all of the preliminary studies indicated this. More tests were undertaken, specifically a large study, the Vioxx Gastrointestinal Outcomes Research Study (called VIGOR), to find out whether Vioxx was less likely to lead to stomach ulcers and bleeding than the drug Naproxen. Heart risks were to be assessed and noted.

In November of 1999, the safety panel for the VIGOR study noticed a disconcerting trend of serious cardiac occurrences in connection with the drug. This added to the suspicion raised by certain preliminary studies. By this time, Vioxx had already been prescribed by doctors for their patients for six months. Instead of issuing a warning, Merck continued to promote Vioxx without one. The drug would lead to untimely deaths, much like Wayne's, at a statistical rate of 21 individuals per day. This would continue for a period of over five years.

One month later, in December of 1999, the VIGOR safety panel was told by researchers that the study was showing the risks of heart attack and stroke were at least twice as high with Vioxx as for those taking Naproxen. Scientists suggested the company analyze the data. The study continued, as did prescriptions, because of a hypothesis company scientists held that Naproxen might have a similar protective benefit for the heart like aspirin, which would account for the larger numbers of cardiac events in Vioxx users. Because of this assumption, patients who were prescribed the drug were expiring from heart attacks and strokes at a statistical rate of 147 individuals per week.

In February of 2000, company scientists agreed to analyze the data, but omitted the cardiac events that happened in the final month of the study. Results of the VIGOR study, minus heart attacks 18, 19, and 20, were submitted to the *New England Journal of Medicine* for publication. Two sets of corrections were made between July and November of 2000, with no mention of the additional heart attacks. The three individuals lost their lives while participating in a research study to assess the safety and effectiveness of a pain reliever that was hoped to be safer than relatively safe medications like ibuprofen and acetaminophen; the information their deaths provided would not even be used by Merck to ensure the safety of the general public.

Merck told the FDA about heart attacks 18, 19, 20 in October of 2000. Nothing was done. Then in November, a year and a half after the drug was approved and the same month Wayne died of sudden myocardial infarction, results of the skewed VIGOR study were published in the *New England Journal of Medicine*. The three heart attacks as well as data on many other kinds of cardiac adverse events had been omitted. These cooked study results were key for Merck to begin aggressively marketing Vioxx to doctors as a drug confirmed to have a favorable cardiovascular safety profile. More and more doctors were convinced to prescribe this breakthrough medication; few if any recognized their patients' serious cardiac occurrences were in any way linked to taking Vioxx. Physicians would be shocked to later learn that these patients were being slain at a statistical rate of at least 633 individuals per month.

The FDA published the complete VIGOR data on its website in February of 2001, including the adverse cardiac results that had been left out by Merck. They also allowed Merck to drop digestive warnings from the label. By August of 2001, independent cardiologists Debabrata Mukherjee, Steven Nissen, and Eric Topol had analyzed the complete data from the FDA's website and published their own meta-analysis in the *Journal of the American Medical Association*. These results cast serious doubt on the assumption Merck officials had made regarding the heart-protective benefit of Naproxen. Authors of the meta-analysis noted, "Given the remarkable popularity of this new class of medications, we believe that it is mandatory to conduct a trial specifically assessing cardiovascular risks and benefits of their agents." Studies to specifically rule out cardiovascular risks would never be undertaken by Merck.

In September of 2001, the FDA sent a letter to Merck complaining that the company was downplaying potential risks and misrepresenting the drug's safety. The FDA expressed significant concern for public health and safety to the company that was selling the drug, but communicated nothing to doctors or to the public. By September 11, 2001, when the deadly terrorist attack took the lives of at least 2,977 innocent civilians, roughly 17,732 lives had been quietly snuffed

147

out by Merck's pain-killer Vioxx. Eleven days after the attack, Tom Ridge was appointed director of the Office of Homeland Security, the bureau set up for safeguarding U.S. citizens and interests from outside threats. In those eleven days following the attack, statistically speaking, 528 individuals would experience serious heart complications and heart attacks from taking Vioxx. Of those, 231 would not survive.

The United States government responded to the terror attacks in October of 2001 by beginning airstrikes against Taliban targets in Afghanistan; the president told the American public that the terrorists would not get away with murder. By July 2014, coalition causalities from ongoing operations in that country would number 3,363. That twelve year total amounted to 435 fewer lives lost than the statistical Vioxx fatalities for the six months between the start of operations in Afghanistan, and April of 2002 when Merck was finally persuaded to attach a heart risk warning to the drug label. In March of 2003, the United States government initiated military action in Iraq. Over nine years coalition forces lost, on average, 45 service members per month equaling a death toll of 4,805 by the time operations were declared over. Mislead by Merck and the FDA, doctors continued prescribing Vioxx to unsuspecting patients who were succumbing to heart attacks and strokes at a statistical rate of 630 individuals per month, and numbered an estimated 3,798 every six months.

From the beginning of 2002 to August 2004, epidemiological studies had continued to indicate that taking Vioxx carried heart risks. Some analysis had showed as much as a five-fold increased risk. Both Merck and the FDA had remained unwilling to kill the drug. In fact, Merck got to work devising clever strategies for their marketing representatives to "dodge" physician questions regarding the heart risks. Whenever outside researchers cast doubt on the safety of Vioxx, Merck officials vehemently disagreed and took immediate action to prevent the incriminating data from being published. During these years, the Homeland Security advisory system issued nationwide alerts from yellow (elevated threat) to orange (high threat) on five occasions. While Americans had been alerted to the outside threat of terror during this two and a half year period, statistically, 19,631 citizens who had been treated with Vioxx were quietly eliminated. Throughout this time the FDA continued to allow Merck to promote Vioxx.

Finally, in September of 2004, Vioxx was voluntarily withdrawn by Merck when their own study for colon polyp prevention confirmed the undeniable risk of heart problems that outside analysts had been warning about. One researcher, Dr. David Graham, was an FDA scientist who had been vocal about the risks but could get no support for his data within the FDA. Merck finally acknowledged the problem, but contended that those who took Vioxx for fewer than 18 months had not been put at risk. Later, outside analysis of this same study strongly suggested that the heart risks began shortly after starting the drug and remained long after patients had stopped taking it. Merck disagreed with this finding, as they had from the beginning, that there was anything wrong with Vioxx. At least 20 million people worldwide had been prescribed the drug in a period of over five years. Research later published in the medical journal, *The Lancet*, estimated that in the least, 88,000 heart attacks and 38,000 deaths had occurred as a result of prescriptions for Vioxx.

For the families of these victims, the only statistic that matters is *one*. Significant for them is the one family member who will not be replaced. Like us, their worlds were irreversibly altered by a senseless loss. Had Wayne taken Vioxx? We don't know. Does it matter? Not really. He's gone, as is every one of the individuals who died because of Vioxx over the course of those five years and maybe beyond. Nothing changes that. But scores of families, like ours, have been left to wonder why a relatively healthy family member ended up so quickly succumbing to a fatal heart attack or stroke. An unimaginable number of families do not know, and will never know, that the pain-killer Vioxx was behind their loved one's death. The time for anyone to know anything about Vioxx would have been way back when Merck was finding it out. Something tells me that every one of the estimated 88,000 people who suffered heart complications or death would have risked developing a stomach ulcer from ibuprofen or aspirin rather than put their family through the pain of serious illness and sudden death.

Unlike the terrorists, Merck certainly didn't intend for anyone to die. In fact, they were wildly wishing upon a star that no one would. They certainly didn't intend to scare anyone, nor did they intend to leave any children fatherless. Yet, while a heart attack may be a far cry

149

from a terror attack, it's chilling to think about how aggressively and deceptively this company operated in order to get Vioxx into the hands of as many doctors and into the bodies of as many patients as they possibly could, all the while dismissing and deflecting attention from the fact that even their own tests had indicated it could cause heart problems. They played a tireless game of hard-ball to assure themselves and their shareholders a bonanza. It was a covert, sustained attack for inflow of cash. The killing may not have been intentional, but it was entirely preventable.

In the end, Merck decided to pay $4.85 billion into a settlement fund to avoid the personal-injury and class-action lawsuits that were beginning to be filed by some of the tens of thousands of victims and their families. They also paid roughly 2 billion in legal fees and fines, which was a real bargain compared to what analysts had first predicted this would cost them. It was just another level in the drug company game, and massive profits from Vioxx were the extra lives they had picked up along the way to cover these routine expenses, safeguarding their own survival in their ongoing mission "to save and improve lives around the world." After the settlement, the company cut their losses, got to work on the research and development of new and exciting drugs, and carried on as if none of it had happened.

A *New York Times* opinion piece that ran on September 12, 2001 titled, "The War Against America: The National Defense," is strangely apt for where we continue to find ourselves in regard to pharmaceuticals. It concludes, "As horrible as it is to imagine, the United States must also consider a future in which the assaults carried out yesterday may be overshadowed by even more lethal nuclear, biological or chemical attacks by terrorists. We have long known that these dangers could be part of our future. It is now clear they may be nearer than most people thought. A concerted national effort to remake the nation's defenses must begin immediately."

PROTECTION AND ADVOCACY

After writing out the grievances and dropping them in the mail, the massive bag of bricks the system had progressively saddled me with felt considerably lighter. I didn't concern myself with whether or not there would be a positive resolution, I was just relieved not to be carrying around the entire weight of the injustice anymore.

If I entertained any hope at all, it was that Disability Rights Ohio might take my report seriously, give me specific information about the rights I thought were violated, and provide support and direction as I negotiated the problems at Cornerstone. I knew it was a long shot, but I also wondered if they might take an interest in what I reported as the systemic causes of harm I had endured from taking my medications as prescribed.

Disability Rights Ohio was federally mandated under the Protection and Advocacy for Individuals with Mental Illness Act (PAMI) to investigate reports of rights violations, abuse, neglect, and injury for persons both in institutional settings and in the community. As Ohio's designated Protection and Advocacy System, they addressed grievances for individuals as well as systemic practices affecting persons receiving mental health services.

The PAIMI Act was signed into law in 1986 to ensure the enforcement of constitutional as well as federal and state statutes for persons with mental conditions who were institutionalized. In 2000, the act was amended to include representation of individuals receiving services in community-based settings. Designated PAIMI agencies have been given the task to gather information from within their communities to find ways to better ensure the health and safety of people receiving services for psychiatric conditions, and advocate for individuals in cases of abuse, serious injury, neglect, and violations of civil rights. They could also determine if legal action is warranted and assist individuals in navigating the process of pursuing legal remedies.

151

Though I was unable to receive a copy of the rights and grievance procedure when I requested it from Cornerstone, I did find out on my own that I had the option of initiating my complaint with outside agencies such as Disability Rights Ohio. Because the law specified a grievance should go to someone other than one mentioned in the grievance, and because of the systemic nature of my complaint, it only made sense that I exercise this option. I decided to forgo talking further with those at Cornerstone, as well as Maggie Kramer at the Hamilton County Board of Mental Health, who had also neglected to make sure I had the client rights and grievance procedure information I had asked for.

I sent my grievances directly to Disability Rights Ohio, as well as to the Ohio Department of Mental Health and Addiction Services. As I had hoped, Disability Rights Ohio was the first to respond.

PART FOUR

THE RESPONSES

"You've really got to start hitting the books because it's no joke out here."

— *Harper Lee*

20

Disability Rights Ohio

Ms. Laurie Oakley   February 27, 2014
3030 Edson St.
Cincinnati, OH 45312

Dear Ms. Oakley:

We received your letter on February 25th, 2014 with concerns and complaints regarding your previous services at Cornerstone and systemic problems that you are seeing within the mental health system as a consumer.

After reviewing your request for services, we are referring you to speak further with Maggie Kramer at the Hamilton County Board of Mental Health & Recovery Board, and the Ohio Department of Mental Health and Addiction Services regarding your complaints toward Cornerstone, as well as the state of Ohio Medical Board regarding your complaints against your previous psychiatrist. You may contact the agencies below:

Hamilton County Board of Mental Health
Ohio Department of Mental Health and Addiction Services
State of Ohio Medical Board

Because Disability Rights Ohio has provided you with this information, your request for services will be closed. Please be advised that this office has a grievance procedure which you may use to dispute the denial or closure of your request or service. If you wish to file a grievance, please see the enclosed sheet for more information.

Sincerely,
C.H. Pinaski
Intake Specialist
Enclosed: Grievance Form

Journal Entry

November 15, 2001

I am stuck in a mode of depression. I am not happy with my life. After all of the medical tests turned up nothing, I had a breakdown of sorts. The rhumatologist actually called me "the vein lady." When I had my appointment at Village Behavioral Health, I told Vicki about his suggestion that my pain is psychosomatic. I mentioned the itching and possible mites in the house, and she told me that it is common for abuse survivors to have sensations that make them think they have bugs crawling on their skin. She prescribed a couple of medications for this, Neurontin and Seroquel to take along with Klonopin. I have definitely felt better after taking them and am able to sleep now. I do still have the pain, though. On Monday I will talk to my therapist.

We also talked about my job and about how I had been doing so much better at drywall. I want that feeling back. I want to be free—free to be me. Working at the school just isn't a good fit. I can bear working there knowing I have a plan to find something else.

I do feel good about the kids, though. Parent-teacher conferences went well and their teachers had only good things to say about them.

Village Behavioral Health

Oakley, Laurie A.
Progress Notes
November 1, 2001
Hour: 9:15
Length: 25
Goal: Control symptoms.

Progress: Depressed mood, poor sleep, multiple somatic symptoms.
Client Report of Current Functioning: I am not doing very well at all.
Observations of Client: Casually dressed, tearful at times, articulate.
Topics Covered/Interventions Used/Client Response: Complains of increased symptoms as noted above. Struggling with several issues including upcoming anniversary of her children's father's death, dissatisfaction with her current job as a school para—feels less valued and less productive. Has been dealing with increased "muscle and vein" pain. She was told she was psychosomatic by a neurologist. Also suspecting "some type of mites" in her house. Set up a "sticky board" to identify mites. No luck. Spent 1 week in local motel to stay away from her house.

Plan: See in two or three weeks.

Changes to Treatment Plan/Diagnosis: Serzone is no longer helpful. Has tried almost all of the newer anti-depressants. All SSRIs induced panic attacks. Client agreed to try Neurontin and Seroquel. Benefits and side effects were explained to client. Verbalized understanding of given information. One month supply of each med called in to the pharmacy. Continue Klonopin as ordered. Encouraged her to contact her therapist.

Meets Medical Necessity for Continued Treatment Due To: Mood disorder, need to monitor medication.

21

Ohio Department of Mental Health and Addiction Services

A FEW WEEKS AFTER RECEIVING the letter from Disability Rights Ohio, I received a phone call from Robin Ketter from the Ohio Department of Mental Health and Addiction Services.

Robin wanted to find out what it was that I wanted. She started by telling me the grievance regarding Dr. Lantz didn't add up. She said that just because I was angry with him for not prescribing Seroquel didn't mean I had been disrespected. (Clearly, I was dealing with a speed reader). I explained to her that the grievance was about his disrespectful manner, and the fact that he did not respect my right to decline the proposed medication. This was something I thought I made clear in the written document. After I explained this, she told me I could take my complaint to the State Medical Board, that doctors take an oath which is their responsibility to uphold, and the agencies don't hold a doctor accountable. I asked her if she was recommending I do that—take it to the State Medical Board—and she replied that she didn't recommend anything one way or another. So I explained that I wasn't as concerned with this particular doctor as I was with the systemic practices that influenced his decisions, those practices being, in large part, due to pharmaceutical influence. I asked her if it was the responsibility of the community mental health systems to ensure clients were protected from this influence. She said it was up to individual doctors and that she could see no way of addressing systemic problems as the agencies were too numerous and in multiple places.

She also told me that Cornerstone's Client Rights Officer had done her due diligence in sending me what she had, even though it was only part of the rights and none of the grievance information. I didn't challenge her on this, but felt compelled to ask her at this point why she was advocating for the agency. She denied she was advocating for the agency and then asked again exactly what it was that I wanted.

I stated that I was simply reporting what had happened to me within the larger system and within this particular agency. I felt what had happened was unjust and these things deserved both attention and a response. I stressed that I was not the only person affected by these practices, and told her I believed those hearing my complaints had a duty to respond. They could decide for themselves what that response should be.

Robin said sure, she could probably talk to the Client Rights Officers about their responsibility to provide client rights and grievance information, but beyond that, there was nothing Ohio Department of Mental Health and Addiction Services could do. She recommended I sign a release form so she could share my information with Maggie Kramer back at the Hamilton County Board of Mental Health.

Maggie had been one of the Client Rights Officers who hadn't recognized my right to receive the written client rights and grievance information when I was asking for it. Neither Disability Rights Ohio or the Ohio Department of Mental Health and Addiction Services even registered this. Nevertheless, Maggie would be my so called advocate. My grievances, including the one she was named in, would soon end up on her desk.

Journal Entry

April 21, 2002

There isn't a shortage of stuff to be done or things I desire to do. It's just that I have no energy. I'm wired and tired, all at the same time. I've felt really stressed but have let go of trying to know what these symptoms are about. I'm still trying to get used to the idea that this is all in my head. I wanted to get off of Seroquel and tried, but cannot quit taking it without itching at night.

My practitioner at Village Behavioral Health told me to stop going off medications on my own. When I joked about wanting to become an alcoholic after feeling more present to the kids after I'd had some wine, she told me just to take more Klonopin. I did try this and felt a little better. I am still taking Neurontin. My new primary care physician suggested an anti-depressant, but I told her they cause panic attacks so she said the Neurontin should help.

I am now working at a press clippings service and this is a good fit for me. It's still difficult trying to balance working and being available to the kids. I was written up after staying home with Grace when she had the flu, on top of my having missed during the city-wide shut down during the ice storm. I can only do what I can do. Bottom line, I will miss work if I need to. Their dad's death benefit gives me options, yet everything changed when he died. It's a free ride with a price.

161

SECONDARY ADDICTIONS

After my symptoms of tolerance withdrawal were misdiagnosed as somatization, I tried to accept that diagnosis. The medications I was given for those symptoms did mask them, at least for a while. I don't remember why I decided to quit taking them, but I do know by now that I'm glad I did. Whenever the tolerance withdrawal symptoms resurfaced, my practitioners were determined to treat them as a primary condition. They were never outwardly disrespectful of me for not sticking with their treatments, but years later after obtaining my medical record, I became aware of their true feelings toward me.

The misdiagnosis of hypochondria took my life down a few notches. There is already enough stigma connected to having mental health issues, but you don't get much lower than being labeled a hypochondriac, especially with health professionals. It was as if my self-esteem had fallen from a second story window.

I began isolating from people and from life. I escaped through my computer by creating a blog which I used to connect to people around the globe with whom I had common interests. While some positive things eventually developed out of this, at the time I was not showing up for my own life. I spent several hours a day on the computer instead of engaging in meaningful activities, socializing, or spending quality time with my kids. Even when I wasn't online, my mind was preoccupied with discussions concerning the war in Iraq or the radical faith communities some of my new friends were a part of. Later, I would learn this was a secondary addiction I used to cope with the misdiagnosis, as well as the ongoing medication side-effects.

I self-medicated with alcohol a number of times, as well as with the pain-killer, hydrocodone, which I had been given a few years earlier for my back injury. These did provide transient relief, but because I had always been cautious about substances I knew could cause addiction, I avoided using them too often. I am fortunate I didn't end up developing a more serious addiction to either alcohol or prescribed medications.

Interestingly, when a patient's dependence upon prescribed medications does progress into drug addiction, doctors are notorious for dumping them. In the case of benzodiazepines, this is especially tragic. Many patients then land in drug rehab centers which end up being less than helpful.

Dr. Ashton warns that detoxification clinics designed to treat those coming off of alcohol and illegal drugs are inappropriate for persons wanting to stop benzodiazepines, as they generally withdraw individuals from benzodiazepines too rapidly. While it is advisable to taper the drugs over a period of several months, rehab centers routinely withdraw them in a matter of days. For many, withdrawal symptoms from benzodiazepines are more severe and longer lasting than with other drugs, even heroin, and users often need specialized support as well as extended follow up. Although entities like the Maine Benzodiazepine Study Group have made attempts to educate doctors about these differences, Dr. Ashton notes that few make use of the information.

My iatrogenic dependence and ongoing tolerance withdrawal remained unrecognized. I spent three more years in this state. With each passing day that the true nature of my problem remained hidden, the medication slowly and steadily continued making changes in my brain. Meanwhile I gravitated toward secondary addictions, never suspecting that a substance that had been expensively developed, researched, and widely marketed to make people's lives better was quietly wreaking havoc in mine.

I ended up taking Klonopin eight full years before I was finally able to discontinue it on my own. (I was told by practitioners that I did not need help coming off half a milligram, but it took me several attempts and much suffering to finally do this). Had I known the severe insomnia I began experiencing when I quit Klonopin was possibly due to functional brain damage and that it would never fully reverse itself, I'm not sure I would have stopped taking it. I can only imagine, though, that I am better off because I did.

22

Hamilton County Board
of Mental Health

WHEN I ARRIVED AT THE Hamilton County Board of Mental Health building, the first thing I did was get into it with the receptionist. Maybe I *was* the problem? I had begun to wonder. She didn't like me leaving my soggy rain gear in their large, plant-filled foyer, but then wouldn't let me throw it back outside with my bike, either. So I told her I would just keep it with me, though she had begrudgingly found a spot for it behind the front desk. She insisted she was only doing me a favor, after which we exchanged a couple of "whatevers," and all this before I had even sat down. If I was already doing this bad with the receptionist, I couldn't wait to see how things would go with Maggie Kramer.

I expected Maggie would be like the others: she probably hadn't read my grievances, nor would she really listen, and she would tell me this or that right had not been, in fact, violated. I was bracing for this and had been coaching myself for days not to react. Interestingly, all of that changed rather quickly.

After introducing herself with a gentle handshake, I followed Maggie as she slowly walked to her office. First things first, she made sure I had a copy of my rights and the grievance procedure. We sat at a table and she faced me, with a pen and paper to take notes. She looked at me when I spoke. She hadn't read the grievances only because they hadn't been sent to her, so I pulled out a copy for each of us and we started from the beginning. Halfway through the first grievance, I paused to thank her for listening, and told her I hadn't expected that she would. She responded by assuring me she was my advocate, but by this time I was wishing she were my grandmother.

When I got to the part that mentioned her, I thought for sure I would lose her, but she continued to remain attentive. If she felt at all defensive, she sure didn't show it. When I needed to pause and gather my thoughts, she did not use it as an opportunity to interject anything. She instead said, "take all the time you need." Her sole focus was hearing my story and understanding where I was coming from. She empathized with my concern over many of the things I told her, the large as well as the smaller problems.

I began to feel silly for typing up a ten page grievance that included complaints of receiving agency identified envelopes that I thought violated my right to privacy, and for submitting them way up the ladder when Maggie had been down here in Cincinnati ready to advocate for me the whole time. Maybe I'd had to move my game piece back several spaces, but like I told her as I put my hand on the clump of papers, we were talking about more than 18 years of my life here.

After fully hearing what I had to say, Maggie explained there were limits to what could be accomplished by filing a grievance with the Hamilton County Board. She used for an example, that if I had wanted a can of pop and staff denied it, I could file a grievance and the board could investigate why I had been denied a pop. I was pretty sure my case was different, but I understood what she was saying.

She reminded me of my polyester-wearing first grade teacher, Miss Starbird in her horn rimmed glasses. She pulled out a colorful diagram to show me where we were in the grievance process. "See, you've already made it this far," she said as she used her pen to point to the pink oval that signified the third step. She asked if I minded if she wrote up a synopsis of my complaints to use as a cover sheet before submitting my grievance to the board president. I said sure. A few weeks later, there would be a hearing, she said.

I felt significantly unburdened after meeting with Maggie and couldn't stop a few tears from mingling with the rain on my bike ride home as I vowed to become that kind of old person. I wasn't sure if they even made them like that anymore, but if they did, I wanted in. She had been a cup of cold water on a hot, hot day. Though the grievance process was turning out to be another road to hell paved with good intentions, Maggie was proof that at least there were rest stops.

Journal Entry

June 12, 2002

Where I am getting this strength I do not know. Patience in suffering is something I seem to be finally learning. I am still dealing with "symptoms" and they seem to be getting worse. The medications really don't help, yet I can't seem to get completely off of them. I wish there was a medication that worked. The Klonopin only helps for a while, and I can't get into the habit of increasing the dose. At Village Behavioral Health I was told to just take everything as prescribed. I don't want to be on all of that and I never feel well on it anyway. I went to my primary care doctor for pain and lack of sleep. She said it could be something related to fibromyalgia.

Right now I just want to maintain consistency for the kids. Both of them are in karate now and we have made some really good friends there. Now that it is summer, the pool is open again. I look forward to taking them and watching them as they pop out of the water shouting, "Marco!"

"Polo!"

Village Behavioral Health

Oakley, Laurie A.
Progress Notes
June 10, 2002
Hour: 2:30
Length: 30
Goal: Medication compliance.
Progress: Stopped portion of meds.

Client Report of Current Functioning: I need support from somewhere.
Observations of Client: Neatly dressed, focusing on tangential issues, tearful.

Topics Covered/Interventions Used/Client Response: Laurie talked about feeling frazzled and how she wishes she had more support. When I inquired about her meds, she stopped taking Klonopin and Seroquel. She also talked about wanting to drink. Encouraged her to identify what her real needs for control are. She will restart her medicine as prescribed. Discussed my leaving. She will think about who she wants as a prescriber.

Plan: See new practitioner in 2 months.

Changes to Treatment Plan/Diagnosis: Added medication compliance issue.

Meets Medical Necessity for Continued Treatment Due To: Impairment in reality testing, impairment in social, familial, academic/work functioning, mood disorder, interpersonal/behavioral difficulties, need to monitor medication.

General Family Practice

Oakley, Laurie A.
Progress Notes
July 23, 2002

S: 36-year-old white female complaining of generalized achiness and pain all over her body which began one year ago and just will not go away. She has undergone extensive evaluation here as well as by the rheumatologist with no exact etiology being found. I think she is very depressed, very anxious. She continues to have trouble sleeping. She is not having any crying spells. We discussed how she has been to several doctors and has tried multiple medications. Every SSRI anti-depressant I listed today she has been on before. She is on Klonopin, Neurontin and Seroquel but continues to have symptoms. Recently the pain seems to have become more constant and worse in degree. She denies any weakness or numbness in any of her extremities. No incoordination. She states "this is not your ordinary aches and pains." She denies recent illness. No fever, chills or sweats. She had a lot of stress when her childrens' father died, however she is doing better in regard to that. She confides in me that she thinks that she could be dying sometimes.

O: Patient is alert and in no acute distress. Lungs are clear and heart is regular.

A: Generalized pain—I would wonder if this is more related to psychosomatic problems.
P: Increase Neurontin to 300mg for 3 days, then 400 mg for five days, then 400 mg twice a day to see if this helps with symptoms. She should follow up in two weeks or as needed.

23

The Hearing

THE THOUGHT OF A HEARING had been by far the most anxiety producing aspect of the grievance process. I never liked being in the spotlight, especially when it was hard to mentally keep track of things and to come up with the right words when I needed them. For weeks, I had imagined the courtroom version, complete with a robed, gavel slamming judge with a sidekick bailiff. As it turned out, it wasn't that big of a deal.

Four of us sat around tables. There was Kim, the hearing officer, Janette, the Rights Officer representing my former Cornerstone practitioners, then Maggie and myself. I was given the opportunity to speak first. There were so many things I wanted to say and I had been encouraged by Maggie to say them, yet she had also explained that freedom from harmful practices was not a grievable right.

Can you tell me how an individual harmed by systemic practices within community mental health agencies can report the life-altering consequences? This was what I wanted to jump to. Instead, I summarized what had happened on the last day I received services.

Can you tell me why a system that brings these treatments into people's lives does not have a protocol for responding to clients or patients who report serious, disabling outcomes? But this meeting wasn't about resolving systemic problems. Still, as I finished summarizing, I emphasized that my story had never been taken seriously enough to be reported by any doctor.

Why is there no looking into my record, verifying and making use of this information? Instead, I focused on Janette, who represented the agency. She began by making two apologies, one for the difficulty I encountered when asking for the written rights and grievance information, and another for the situations that left me feeling that my doctors had not listened.

If not the doctors, then who? Who can help me get my report of harm to the right people or person or system? My thoughts remained on systemic concerns as she continued. In regard to Dr. Lantz, she said he told her he discussed many different treatment options with me, and while it was my right not to follow his recommended treatment, she backed him in sticking with the treatment decision he felt was right. Agencies do not question doctors' treatment decisions but do address matters of disrespect, she said.

Are you aware of corporate drug industry influence in the education of doctors and in the science that gets drug treatments approved? Then, in regard to the therapist, Janette said she stood behind Lynn's clinical decision not to co-treat, and said my work with the trauma specialist could "filter in." When the hearing officer inquired if I could have been given case management services instead of termination, Janette said yes, that would have been an option. Did I have any questions? No. Not about this, anyway.

Who is responsible for protecting individuals from agency practitioners who are unaware of the ways in which their profession is influenced by industry? We had a back and forth discussion. Janettte explained the principle of staying with one doctor and not switching. She said that a person will often end up having a similar problem with a new doctor so they require clients to stick with one and work things out. While it was obvious I wanted a change because Dr. Lantz had been disrespectful, I explained that I had only made a prior switch after a break from services, and mostly because Dr. Elliot had been fresh out of ideas. I told them Dr. Elliot seemed to care about my situation but I was frustrated that he hadn't taken it seriously enough to report it to anyone.

Right now, studies are being undertaken to determine if a medication like Klonopin might be a potential long-term treatment for the many individuals who struggle with autistic behaviors. Would you let a doctor put your family member who experiences significant barriers to communication on a drug whose side-effects are often vague, universally misunderstood, and vastly underreported? After we hashed out agency matters, I said I didn't care so much about what had happened between myself and the two practitioners, but wanted to know how my report of harm could be recognized. We discussed Klonopin and someone mentioned addiction, and they talked about how their agency doctors don't prescribe it. I pointed out that there is much more to it than addiction, and then brought up industry influence. They listened. But when I asked who is responsible for hearing these concerns within the system and doing something about it, they seemed as clueless as I was.

By the end of our time, I'd had a chance to voice all of my concerns and they had respectfully listened. The hearing officer thanked me for bringing these things to the attention of the board, and suggested maybe a grassroots advocacy organization like the National Alliance on Mental Illness might be worth looking into. NAMI was excellent, she said, with members taking collective action, going before legislators at both state and national levels to see the changes in the system that they wanted to see.

This was difficult. I knew she meant well. They all did. Even the cranky doctor who for all I knew still had student loans coming out the wazoo. But in this context, grassroots activism was far from a justifiable suggestion. The average Joe with a mental health condition was already facing a battle. Then comes a drug treatment that was sold as helpful only to cause further disability which is then completely denied by practitioners. Why on earth would the systems that usher these treatments into people's lives rely upon patients and their families joining grassroots organizations so that those in Washington might finally force them to take patients seriously? As well meaning as it was, coming from the county board this was a ridiculous non-solution.

As for the National Alliance on Mental Illness, NAMI had been a true grassroots organization for about five minutes in the late 1970's. In 1999, a senate probe revealed that the lion's share of their funding had been coming from the pharmaceutical industry. I had a good friend who was a member of NAMI and knew they could have a positive influence. But I also knew that an organization funded heavily by the drug industry and whose political actions consistently resulted in legislation that increased that industry's bottom line was not about to throw the truck in reverse in response to my story or that of anyone else.

Even if I had wanted to run into NAMI's open arms, it wasn't a likely proposition. I valued activism but barely had the energy to get out of bed in the morning. Now, rounding third base of the grievance process, all I could think of was sliding into home. Once there, the only thing I'd be up for would be a dirt nap.

Journal Entry

February 2, 2003

I would like to avoid over-medicating.

I want to be sure of who I am.

I would like to be less anxious.

I want to quit blaming.

I would like to pursue my interests.

I want to be loyal.

I would like to live my life instead of avoiding.

I want to quit being disappointed.

I would like to be a better friend.

I want to set a few goals.

I would like to stop being scared when I wake up at night.

I want the nagging feelings that censor me to either correct me or stop.

I would like to be emotionally healthy.

I want to be a giver, not a taker, and I want to be aware if I'm taking.

I would like to be more available to my children.

I want to be well.

Village Behavioral Health

Oakley, Laurie A.
Progress Notes
February 5, 2003
Hour: 11:00
Length: 44
Goal: Medication compliance

Progress: Not accomplished

Client Report of Current Functioning: It could be worse. More depressed than usual.

Observations of Client: Casual, good insight.

Topics Covered/Interventions Used/Client Response: Client reports low energy and increased anxiety. States Seroquel makes her feel too sedated. Has experienced increased guilt feelings and some panic as well. Went through the entire list of anti-depressants and found that she's been on all except MAOIs and TCAs. Discussed supply problems with MAOIs. Gave her educational handout on TCAs. She has a good grasp of the information.

Plan: PRN.

Changes to Treatment Plan/Diagnosis: Seroquel 12.5 mg if she chooses, Neurontin 300 mg daily from PCP, Klonopin 1 mg.

Meets Medical Necessity for Continued Treatment Due To: Mood disorder, need to monitor medication.

SLEEPWALKING

"*If* that really happened to you, it was awful," a woman in my writer's group told me. She was a healthcare worker, yet this response was typical. Both inside and outside of medical circles, mine was apparently a strange case. For some unknown reason my story wasn't something people could readily believe or relate to, let alone a matter that required attention or action.

I couldn't help but wonder, though, if ultimately we were not all in the same boat. Sure, most people went to doctor appointments, took medications as prescribed, and usually got better. At least for a while. Yet I wondered how many health conditions were manufactured (unintentionally I presume), like mine had been? I wondered, if people were to become aware of the exact nature of some of the illnesses they suffered, might they become compelled to do something different? Didn't they at least have a right to know?

When it came to selling products that might be making us sick, the pharmaceutical industry was far from the only culprit. The food industry routinely added synthetic chemicals to processed foods; many items were genetically modified as well. Most convenience foods were then packaged in plastics which could leach additional toxins into the food. Unlike with pharmaceuticals, people at least had an inkling that most of these products were not intended to improve our health, although conducting thorough studies to determine long-term risks hadn't been a top priority of food manufacturers, either. Certain products identified as particularly harmful, such as hydrogenated oils and aspartamine, had still been approved by the FDA and therefore, most people felt comfortable consuming them.

Families spent quality time over dinners made with a wide selection of fruits and vegetables that had been sprayed liberally by the agriculture industry with herbicides and pesticides. I wondered if the science behind the use of these chemicals mirrored what I had learned about pharmaceuticals? People consumed meats containing antibiotics and fillers, and dairy products that contained growth hormones. The treats we gave our children, signifying our love, were often made with genetically modified ingredients and packed with sugar or high fructose corn syrup, colorful dyes, preservatives, and other additives.

I wondered about industrial companies including steel mills, pulp and paper factories, and chemical and pesticide manufacturers, that continually discharged millions of pounds of chemicals and carcinogenic releases into our increasingly damaged waterways. Every year, large volumes of toxic chemicals ended up in rivers, streams, lakes, and ocean waters from gas and oil drilling, oil refineries, as well as uranium, copper, and gold mining. Why did the EPA allow heavy doses of toxic waste from hydraulic fracturing and other industries to be injected into aquifers from which they were likely to end up in wildlife habitats as well as in human water supplies? In addition to all of these pollutants, populations large and small were being exposed to trace pharmaceuticals in drinking water, the outcomes of which were unknown. Could the millions of pounds of toxic chemicals that resulted in oxygen depleted dead zones in waterways be something we might want to pay attention to? A better question might be, how could they not be?

Tons of radioactive water spilled from Fukushima's damaged nuclear power plant while the Japanese government assured their citizens the food was safe. General Electric and the nuclear industry continued to promote nuclear energy as environmentally friendly while other plants, in the US and elsewhere, sat like time bombs on fault lines, ill equipped to withstand similar disasters.

While coral reefs were dying, honeybees were disappearing, and the extinction of several species of plants, insects, and animals were occurring, disease rates for multiple types of cancer, heart disease, and diabetes continued to rise despite advances in medicine. Reproductive and other disorders linked to endocrine disruptors increased, yet people failed to make a connection. As with smoking, the damage accumulated over time. By the time a disease manifested, exposure had long since occurred while other exposures continued.

What were the long-term implications for infants exposed in uetro and born addicted to anti-depressants, narcotics, and other medicines prescribed during pregnancy? What did it mean for those whose mother's breast milk showed traces of glyphosphate from agricultural spraying, among other synthetic chemicals? While developmental disorders were a known outcome of exposure to various substances, a clear connection of specific causation was rarely possible.

"Everyone's gotta die of something," we sometimes said as we reached for vices like cigarettes, pop, and drive thru fast foods. Others didn't care to know or didn't really mind, as my friend Nick put it, to be killed by convenience. Yet how different it felt for those of us who believed in the process of informed consent and the consumer's right to know, only to find out that almost everything we were being sold, from healthcare to war, was exposing the world to toxins that over time would make everyone sicker. And it was only natural in the course of business for corporations to actively prevent us from seeing this or from utilizing other options.

As Jared Diamond pointed out in his book, *Collapse: How Societies Choose to Fail or Succeed*, it was an error to expect corporations to act like charities. The owners of mining companies "couldn't afford" to protect the public from toxic metals leaching year after year from their abandoned mines, just like chemical manufacturers, including the pharmaceutical industry, didn't find the time or money to adequately test their products for long-term adverse effects.

Industries existed for one purpose: to make money. Lots of it. Sure, they sold themselves as having your best interest, but that was just the hook. Afterward you were dragged in the street, and if they had played their cards right, you *liked* it. Even setting my bad experiences aside, a close look at corporatist behavior showed their steadfast allegiance was not to the public but to shareholders. To economic growth. Always. What trickled down was misery with taxpayers cleaning up the messes, when they could be cleaned up at all.

When I was able to see this bigger picture, I took strange comfort in the fact that even those with an overblown sense of entitlement, those who couldn't bring themselves to care and who marched on with their lives as if they were somehow more deserving, would eventually succumb like the rest of us. The deer in headlights looks I received, and the "you could never teach me anything" attitude I got from

179

people when I related my story, continually sucked the air out of me. Yet, could I really blame anyone who was, like me, recently born into this insane culture? I had to admit I shared some of those same characteristics even after my own unfortunate experiences. In the end we were only human. Just messy humans doing what messy humans do. So, of course I blamed them.

24

The Findings

Ms. Laurie Oakley   May 20, 2014
3030 Edson St.
Cincinnati, OH 45312

Dear Ms. Oakley;
The following is a response to your Client Rights Grievance.

Hearing Held: May 13, 2014
Persons Present:
Grievant:: Ms. Laurie Oakley
Respondent:: Ms. Janette Williamson, Client Rights Officer
(Cornerstone).
Client Rights Officer: Ms. Maggie Kramer, Hamilton County Mental
Health and Recovery Services Board.
Hearing Officer: Ms. Kim Hartwell, Hamilton County Mental Health
and Recovery Services Board.

The following document is being written as a result of the hearing in
the matter of your grievance against Cornerstone concerning the
violation of your client rights. Specifically, you stated that Client
Rights #1, #11, #20, #21, and #24 were violated while being a client of
Cornerstone. In order to be consistent with the grievance document
submitted to the Hamilton County Mental Health and Recovery

Services Board, findings will be rendered in the following order: Client Rights #11, #20,#24, #21, and #1. All rights quoted are based on the current Cornerstone Client Rights for Ohio Department of Mental Health Sites (Standard 5122-26-18).

Findings:

Client Right #11: The right to give full informed consent to any service including medication prior to commencement and the right to decline services including medications absent an emergency.

There was no finding in regard to Client Right #11 because it was difficult to determine the exact interaction with Dr. Lantz. The grievant perceived a negative response to her decision not to take the medication Trazodone. Ms. Oakley reported that she was not given credit for trying the medication and she felt that her symptoms and history with medication problems were ignored and rejected.

Recommendation: Despite the lack of a formal finding with regard to Client Right #11, it is recommended that the interactions in this situation be reviewed for any learning about how it may have been handled in a way to help Ms. Oakley to feel heard and respected in her right to decline the medication Trazodone.

Client Right #20: The right to exercise rights without reprisal in any form including the ability to continue services with uncompromised access. No right extends so far as to supersede health and safety considerations.

The finding was found in favor of the respondent in that there is no written or verbal evidence that Cornerstone intentionally acted in a manner to punish Ms. Oakley for exercising her rights by discontinuing her access to services.

Client Right #24: The right to be informed in advance of the reason(s) for discontinuance of service provision, and to be involved in planning for the consequences of that event.

The finding was found in favor of the grievant in that information was presented to Ms. Oakley in a manner that did not completely inform her in advance of the reason(s) for the discontinuance of her service provision or the options available to possibly avoid the discontinuance of her service provision. The presentation of the information therefore impacted her ability to be fully aware of the options available to her in planning for the consequence of service discontinuation.

This finding is based upon two separate occurrences in Ms. Oakley's treatment. First, Ms. Oakley upon asking to be switched to a different psychiatrist was informed that "Cornerstone had already accommodated her in switching her once and that they (Dr. Lantz) had never heard of any case where Cornerstone switched a patient twice both at a patients request." She was also informed that "it was her right to seek a psychiatrist outside of Cornerstone as well." While it should be acknowledged that Ms. Oakley was given a follow up appointment after this exchange of information, it should be noted that Ms. Oakley in her grievance interpreted the information that was shared as she "should find a provider (psychiatrist) outside of the agency."

Recommendation: It is recommended that Cornerstone review its practice for sharing information about options for psychiatric services when there is a request to switch a psychiatrist. During the hearing it was shared that Dr. Allen Wiley reviews all requests to switch psychiatrists and perhaps it would have been sufficient to inform Ms. Oakley of the review process and therefore help her to more freely explore her options around the possibility of the discontinuation of her psychiatry services through Cornerstone.

The second incident that impacted her ability to be informed in advance of the reasons for discontinuance of service provision (psychiatry and therapy) and to be involved in the planning of that event occurred when Ms. Oakley shared with her therapist (Ms. Merek) that she had begun "seeing a trauma specialist." Ms. Merek shared her belief with Ms. Oakley that seeing two therapists was "inappropriate and unethical" and "can be counterproductive as they may have different ways of approaching topics and may contradict one another. " When Ms. Oakley stated she wanted to see Ms. Merek for "symptom management" and the "trauma specialist for childhood issues," Ms. Merek suggested she "could use the trauma specialist for both issues" but in doing so she would not be able to see the psychiatrist (because Cornerstone is not a medication only provider). Ms. Merek explained that Ms. Oakley "could ask her PCP for the Seroquel." When Ms. Oakley chose the other therapist, Ms. Merek explained that her "case would be closed with Cornerstone but she would have the option of returning in the future when her work with the other therapist was finished." Ms. Merek noted that Ms. Oakley would talk to her PCP about medication and she did not make another appointment. Ms. Merek followed up by sending a letter two weeks later that stated since Ms. Oakley had "not contacted the office" she assumed she had begun services with someone else and "was now receiving her psychotrophic medications through her PCP." During the hearing Ms. Oakley stated she did not have medical insurance and therefore did not have a designated PCP with whom she could definitively consult regarding the Seroquel. Ms. Merek was not present in the hearing to offer additional information about Ms. Oakley's understanding of the discontinuation of services and agreement to connect to her primary physician.

Recommendation: It is recommended that Cornerstone review its practice for sharing all options to a client when one service (such as therapy) impacts the provision of another service (such as psychiatry). During the hearing it was shared that perhaps Ms. Oakley could have been considered for case management which would have given her the opportunity to continue receiving psychiatry services through Cornerstone. In this instance if the option of case management had been offered, Ms. Oakley could have been better informed to plan regarding the continuation of services. It is also recommended that the discontinuation letter be reviewed for whether the language could have been changed to offer Ms. Oakley the opportunity to respond instead of stating her services had been closed since it was based upon assumptions regarding her connection to treatment.

Client Right #21: The right to have the opportunity to consult with independent specialists or legal counsel, at one's own expense.
The finding was found in favor of the grievant in that because Ms. Oakley chose the trauma therapist instead of her Cornerstone therapist she was not given the opportunity to pursue other treatment services such as case management and that impacted her ability to access psychiatry services. This finding is not based on the clinical decision to not engage in co-treatment which clinically can be counterproductive to some clients but rather the inadvertent impact it had on Ms. Oakley's right to access other services within Cornerstone.
Recommendation: As stated earlier, it is recommended Cornerstone

review its practice for sharing information about all options available to a client when the discontinuation of one service potentially impacts another service.

Client right #1: The right to be informed of all rights prior to consent to proceed with services, and the right to request a written copy of those rights.

The finding was found in favor of the grievant in that Ms. Oakley did not receive a complete client grievance packet. The packet Ms. Oakley received was missing client rights #1-14, a complete listing of persons available to assist in filing the grievance, namely Ms. Janette Williamson name and contact information as the Cornerstone client rights officer along with the site client rights officer information, and a complete description of what was to occur after she filed her grievance.

Recommendation: It is recommended that Cornerstone review and improve their process for compiling, storing, and distributing client grievance packets to ensure they have the proper grievance information. Specifically, each client grievance packet should contain a complete list of client rights, a complete listing of persons who can receive client grievances along with their contact information, a description in client friendly language of what is to occur after filing the grievance (grievance procedure), and the Client grievance forms. It is also recommended that Cornerstone review its process of posting client rights and client rights officer information and review their training protocols with staff about responding to client rights requests. It is noted that Janette Williamson (Cornerstone) has already agreed to review the following practices:

1. Posting of client rights information and provision of complete client rights packets at Cornerstone treatment sites.

2. Offering of alternative services when one service is discontinued.

3. Discussing with Dr. Fink the possibility of a psychiatrist change review in the event Ms. Oakley would qualify for case management and choose to return to Cornerstone for psychiatric services.

As a resolution, it is suggested that the above recommendations be completed by Cornerstone.

You may ask for further review of this grievance by Cornerstone or with an outside entity. A list is enclosed. The Board will cooperate in providing information about the grievance to the outside entity at your request.

Sincerely,
Kim Hartwell
Hearing Officer, Hamilton County Mental Health and Recovery Services Board

Journal Entry

July 30, 2003

Nature was good to me today. I walked on the trails at the old Menninger Foundation where the kids' dad and I used to go with them. At first it was just Grace, and later we took both kids in front packs or the back carrier. We hiked with them up the steep path through the quiet woods. Their dad actually ran all the way up that steep incline with Marley in the carrier once. After he died, the roll of film found left in his camera contained photos he had taken there—of a deer, fall foliage, and even a skunk.

While walking the path, I heard drops of rain falling lightly in the trees. In the field of tall, bronze grass by the pond, an elegant pair of geese landed to rest. Canadian geese have always been my favorite. Flying in their "V," they look out for each other, and if one lags behind, a friend will stay with him.

I thought about my life, and the lives of others—the greed plagued rich, the poor being crushed by them, the lives of indigenous tribes who once lived where I stood, and the lives of struggle for so many living in the so-called developing nations. Developing into what, I wonder. From within the protection of the grove of trees, I could hear the stream of large trucks roaring in the distance on I-70—heavy trucks transporting things excavated from an overtaxed earth.

So much loss, so much losing, so much to let go of, and how to hold on in a world where everything is constantly and rapidly changing.

187

Village Behavioral Health

Oakley, Laurie A.
Progress Notes
July 28, 2003
Hour: 4:15
Length: 15
Goal: Medication compliance

Progress: Not meeting.

Client Report of Current Functioning: The panic only happens at night
.

Observations of Client: Casual, euthymic.

Topics Covered / Interventions Used / Client Response: Stopped Neurontin in February. Only takes Klonopin now. Awakens at night at 3 a.m. with "panic attack." Discussed sleep disorders and addiction/habituation to benzodiazepines.

Plan: See in 3 months.

Changes to Treatment Plan/Diagnosis: Klonopin 1 mg daily. Can try taper if Ambien works. Ambien 10 mg ½ PRN for insomnia.

Meets Medical Necessity for Continued Treatment Due To: Mood disorder, need to monitor medication.

25

The Final Analysis

B Y THE END OF IT, I wasn't quite sure what to make of the whole grievance process. After receiving the letter from Disability Rights Ohio that bumped me back down to Maggie Kramer, I wrote them a short letter politely asking why they would not investigate the matter of harmful medication treatments. There was no reply. I wrote a similar letter to Robin Ketter at the Ohio Department of Mental Health and Addiction Services. I would never hear from her again, either. Both of those agencies had informed me of my right to take the complaint against the doctor to the State Medial Board. What did I look like, the Energizer Bunny?

So, while the policy of informing clients of their right to submit to outside agencies looks good on paper and gives the impression there are safeguards within the system, for me, utilizing this right was no more effective than asking a cloudless sky to produce rain.

When meeting with Maggie that first time, I did wonder if it had been necessary to submit my grievances above her. But these were *their* rules I was trying to follow. As much as I liked Maggie, she was one of the CROs who hadn't taken my right to have written information seriously. She could not be an impartial advocate. She had been a very good listener but ended up leaving important information off of the synopsis that was submitted to the board. Some of the rights I stated had been violated were missing, as well as her own involvement in neglecting to send me the information. (I had an opportunity to read and sign off on the synopsis before she submitted it, but I overlooked the first of these two things and didn't care about the second). At the hearing she said very little. Later, when I remembered some of the issues I had written in the grievances but had forgotten to raise at the hearing, I was frustrated that my advocate had been so silent. When I called her the following day to ask if she would mind sharing from her notes since I couldn't recall everything we had covered, she simply replied, "We don't do that."

The first and only impartial person I encountered in this entire process was Kim Hartwell, the hearing officer. During introductions she had mistakenly thought I was one of the advocates, yet being informed I was a client didn't diminish her respect for me. While the gargantuan issue of pharmaceutical influence would not be addressed by her, she quickly recognized that several of my rights had been violated. I credit her for the findings, almost all of which went in my favor. Initially, it seriously vexed me to read my former practitioners' alterations of the truth, apparently to cover their tracks. Later, though, I realized their statements hadn't made a bit of difference in the outcome. Someone, probably Kim, recognized that best practices don't include shoving an individual around irregardless of that person's feelings. If only the multiple Client Rights Officers I'd contacted in my efforts to be heard had held a similar standard.

In this particular corner of the system I found no true advocates, most were merely checkpoints. CROs trying to figure out how to stop this in its tracks. I made them nervous. I was like an Occupier in their system who they needed to police until I could be pacified or simply gave up. Not that this was intentional, but they consistently put up barricades to keep me corralled. Clearly was lost any sense that I was their fellow citizen and equal.

The behavior of these "advocates" conveyed to me that I was a stranger and an enemy. Someone they didn't want to know. A client with mental diagnoses which may have even included the worst personality disorder. To them, I was a difficult patient raising Cain. Making trouble for what, maybe for the kick of it? I was up to something and possibly even lying. I was a problem that needed to go away.

Undercurrents of stigma dug deeply into my sense of being a person worthy of serious consideration. I struggled to maintain a positive sense of self as CROs were both violating my rights and telling me my rights had not been violated at the same time. Still, I had wanted to believe these were minor concerns. My true intention had always been to let the pharmaceutical piece see the light of day. It wasn't until after I read the findings that I realized just how important all of these other issues had been. Kim Hartwell's letter restored a portion of my dignity that I hadn't even realized had been taken. I'd told myself I would be fine no matter what the outcome and to an extent that was true. But it wasn't until so many of the findings turned up in my favor that I began to realize just how destructive this system, up to and including the grievance process, had been.

After receiving the final letter explaining the findings, I would hear nothing more from any of them again. And that was fine with me. While it might seem odd that I would spend such considerable effort on the grievance process only to abandon ship in the end, there was no way I would be going back. I'd already spent too much time in their wretched Hotel California. What I had written in the grievances was true: these things simply needed to be said. In this matter I was akin to the one doctor I liked best, the fictional, chain smoking Dr. Becker down in the Bronx who was forever telling his assistant, "It's the principle, Margret!"

Journal Entry

September 24, 2004

Change. I do want to change. I want to do the work. I can safely say the path of least resistance is the path I have currently chosen. The more I give in to that, the harder it becomes to do anything. I am slowly but steadily losing.

Change. I can't just sit back and wait for things to fall into place, and I am not helpless. The idea that no matter what I do or don't do, that my life is beyond my control just doesn't work for me anymore.

I let my prescription for Klonopin run out but couldn't sleep, and when I tried to get some to get through the weekend, I was told to wait until my appointment next week. I feel like a junkie dependent on those who supply it, and they seem to view me that way, too. It makes me angry, how degrading this is. I'm serious about getting off of this stuff and hopefully out of their system.

The kids are sensitive to me always being tired, and they try to comfort me when that isn't their job. I'm the one who needs to be here for them. We are getting support. They both have good matches in the Big Brother's Big Sister's program; parenting alone isn't easy but at least Mike and Lola spending time with them regularly gives them something. And this gives me so much peace of mind. They will never know.

Village Behavioral Health

Oakley, Laurie A.
Discharge Summary
March 1, 2005
Admit Date: 3-28-97
Last Contact: 10-5-04

Discharge Diagnosis: Major Depression, recurrent, moderate, with psychotic features; Personality disorder NOS with avoidant and dependent features; relationship loss.

Presenting Problem at Intake: Client was seeking services for assistance with increased symptoms of depression.

Service Modalities Utilized: Pharmacotherapy; Individual Therapy

Overall Goal Progress: Good

Symptom/Problem improvement: Good

Treatment Compliance: Good

Appointment Attendance: No or few missed appointments

Notes: Client has not contacted for services in over 90 days
Treatment Outcome: Dropped out ASA

Treatment Incomplete

RESOLUTION

"The insects are huge and the poison's all been used
and the drugs won't kill your day job."

— Beck Hansen

IT SOUNDS CRAZY AND IT WAS. The human race had gone off the rails. In a relatively short period of time, complex systems had been developed that existed to serve global corporate interests, systems that depended on the destruction of people, other systems, creatures, and the natural world. There were studies that showed all exceedingly successful organisms tended to pass the point of flourishing only to die in their own waste. Whatever. I wasn't born to contradict or fix this. I had a life to live, and more specifically, days to get through.

There was no way to hold the medical or mental health systems or anyone in them accountable. All they offered me was more misery. I refused their drug treatments and they refused to acknowledge they had caused harm. No one would go to jail, no one would be fined, no real changes would be made to the systems that had carelessly gutted my brain. Yet, if I were to cultivate the one medicinal herb I knew could soothe my racing nervous system, I would prosecuted.

Mainstream doctors waste no time detailing the risks of this drug. Cannabis is a Schedule I controlled substance alongside hardcore drugs like heroin and LSD. Groups like the Connecticut State Medical Society recognize it as a dangerous chemical with life-altering properties. There is deep concern among many physicians worldwide for the grave danger it poses to patients who might use it medicinally, even for pain, nausea and vomiting, or glaucoma.

A primary concern is that, unlike conventional drugs, cannabis has not passed the rigorous scrutiny of scientific investigation and therefore cannot be deemed a safe and effective treatment, as are the mainstream drugs that are proved safe through hard science.

While studies to show efficacy are lacking for Dr. Mark L. Kraus of Connecticut, he leads the way in expressing particular concern about the harm caused from smoking marijuana. He states, "Current findings indicate that the evidence suggests that the marijuana cigarette, in contrast with the tobacco cigarette, delivers over four times the amount of tar and much higher concentration of polycyclic aromatic hydrocarbons, such as the carcinogen benzopyrene." Other concerns linked to smoking the drug were that it caused inflammation in the lining of the lungs and that it substantially reduced a person's ability to fight infection and tumors in the lungs. Additionally, acute and chronic bronchitis from smoking marijuana could lead to pneumonia.

Aside from risks to the lungs, there is also concern about tachy-cardia and abrupt changes in blood pressure, a grave concern for those with cardiovascular disease. There is even scientific evidence that long-term smoking of the drug alters the reproductive system, according to Dr. Kraus.

Associations of contemporary medicine and pharmacology remind patients that modern conventional medicine is based upon the application of scientific principles. Extensive clinical research is undertaken to determine the safety and efficacy of all pharmaceuticals, and there are simply no uses for cannabis that there isn't an already well accepted, well researched and more effective treatment.

As one of many practicing physicians and a concerned members of his community, Dr. Kraus further writes, "We must reject these efforts to give marijuana medical credibility by equating it with other more pharmacologically advanced drugs that have passed the rigors of scientific investigation/research and demonstrate significant efficacy in treating illness/conditions."

According to many doctors, there is clear evidence that patients can become dependent upon the drug. Dr. Carrie Borchardt, president of the Minnesota Psychiatric Society, says that states that have legalized the medicinal use of the drug observe an increased risk of addiction. She also added that patients being treated for pain or anxiety could easily be faking those conditions. "It appears that there is a lot of recreational use under the guise of medical marijuana," she said.

Once addiction takes hold, doctors express concerns that individuals will continue using cannabis while putting their education, jobs, interpersonal relationships, legal status, and even lives at significant risk. Marijuana may double the risk of accidents, say researchers at the University of Columbia. Of particular concern are auto accidents. Several studies conducted on the subject have found that drivers who use marijuana are significantly more likely to become involved in a crash.

Dr. Guohua Li, professor of Epidemiology at Columbia University has stated, "Given the ongoing epidemic of drug-impaired driving and the increased permissibility and accessibility of marijuana for medical use in the U.S., it is urgent that we better understand the role of marijuana in causing car accidents."

There are many doctors who worry about public safety and public health implications. Dr. J. Michael Bostwick, a professor of psychiatry at the Mayo Clinic College of Medicine in Rochester says physicians are frustrated that legalization efforts are moving forward despite a lack of research. "The states have caved to political expediency and have legalized medical marijuana–again, in the absence of scientific data."

When considering the children who are given the drug to successfully control severe seizure disorders when nothing else works, doctors are still hesitant. Dr. Bostwick speaks for many doctors when he says, "We realize the pediatric brain is one of the most susceptible to the side effects from marijuana. It's just very difficult for us."

Most of these physicians recall their duty to the Hippocratic Oath in light of the manifold dangers of viewing cannabis as medicine. To them, it would be unthinkable to put this drug in a similar category as pharmaceuticals when it is a doctor's first priority to "do no harm." Good to know.

Finally, informed consent. I scrounged up the cash for a quality vaporizer and found myself a reliable source. I can't say all my problems ended, or that this was even the solution I had been looking for. But in the culture of pharmaceutical ads, where the people are always smiling and the drugs always work—a culture that can't be bothered with those of us who live in the hell of black box warnings and the hell of no warning at all—at least I was *finally* getting some sleep.

EPILOGUE

Marley and Grace,   *July 2014*

Did I ever tell you about my first experience at arm wrestling? It is not a particularly fond memory nor poignant one, but I thought of it the other day.

Extended family was visiting our house when I was about seven. It was decided by someone, I don't remember who, that us kids should arm wrestle. I didn't know what arm wrestling was but like a typical seven-year-old I became really excited about it. Matched against my cousin Steve who was my own age, I sat across from him gripping his right hand in mine with our left hands locked at the fingers under the table. (You have to remember, I knew nothing about this game).

When my uncle Frank shouted go, I didn't know what to do so I pushed my cousin's fist with mine until his knuckles neared the table. Then I thought this was too easy, so I let up and our arms returned to vertical. We continued to push our sweaty, gripped fists back and forth, one way and then the other, while I remained unsure of just how this game was played. I decided to let him push my arm down. Maybe this was what I was supposed to do. When my knuckles hit, the room erupted in cheers. Now it was over and I finally understood.

I've approached many things in life the way I did that arm wrestling match. Like a perpetual seven-year-old, most of the time I'm not sure what I've gotten myself into or just how to play, and often it's not until something is over that I think I might finally understand the game. Looking back, maybe winning should have been easy, but by now I've just learned to consider myself lucky I got to play. As for my cousin, they never stopped cheering. He grew up to become —a doctor.

APPENDIX

Dr. Elliot's Brilliant Suggestions

After explaining how medications had completely disrupted my brain in 1996 in the doctor prescribed two week adjustment period to tolerate SSRI side-effects:

"If the medication caused you to feel so bad, why didn't you just stop taking it?"

After I expressed frustration that the systems in which I was harmed and of which he is a part fail to acknowledge or even make an attempt at inquiry into my horrific experience:

"Maybe you could do like Peter Breggin and write a book about it."

SOURCES AND FURTHER READING

Chapter 2

Breggin, P.R. "An Examination of Eli Lilly and Company's Contentions that the BJ Prozac Documents were Never Missing and Have No Significance." *Psychiatric Drug Facts*. 1996-2014. Web 23 July 2014.

Hyman, Steven E; Nester, Eric J. "Initiation and Adaption: A Paradigm for Understanding Psychotropic Drug Action." *The American Journal of Psychiatry*. Vol 153(2) 151-162, 1996.

Rottenberg, J. "Listening to Prozac, but Hearing Placebo." *Psychology Today*. 20 Feb. 2010. Web 23 July 2014.

Chapter 3

Breggin, P. R. *"Medication Madness: A Psychiatrist Exposes the Dangers of Mood-Altering Medications."* New York: St. Martin's Press, 2008.

Carlson, K. L. "Psychiatric Drugs, Violence and Suicide." *CCHR International*. July 2009. Web 02 June 2014.

"Dangerous Prescription: How Independent Is the FDA?" *PBS Frontline*. 13 Nov. 2003. Web. 23 July 2014.

Reinberg, S. "Debate Builds Over Drug Companies' Fees to FDA." *ABC NEWS*. 23 Mar. 2008. Web 23 July 2014.

Chapter 5

Breggin, P. R. *"Medication Madness: A Psychiatrist Exposes the Dangers of Mood-Altering Medications."* New York: St. Martin's Press, 2008.

Carlson, K. L. "Psychiatric Drugs, Violence and Suicide." *CCHR International*. July 2009. Web 02 June 2014.

Chapter 7

Healy, David. *"The Antidepressant Era."* Cambridge, Mass: Harvard University Press, 1997.

Schafer A. "Biomedical conflicts of interest: a Defense of the Sequesteration Thesis—Learning From the Cases of Nancy Olivieri and David Healy. The Olivieri Symposium." *J Med Ethics* (2004): 30:8-24.

Chapter 9

Dunn, Andrea L., Madhukar H. Trivedi, and Heather A. O'Neal. "Physical Activity Dose—Response Effects on Outcomes of Depression and Anxiety." *Medicine & Science in Sports & Exercise,* 2001.

Chapter 10
Ashton, C. H. "Benzodiazepines: How They Work and How to Withdraw."
The Ashton Manual, 2002.
Maine Benzodiazepine Study Group. University of Maine Center on Aging,
Oct. 2011. Web. 05 June 2014.

Chapter 11
Akadjian. "Case Studies in Activism #67: Battling Big Pharma and
Rehumanizing Mental Health Treatment." *Daily Kos.* Mar. 2014. Web
June 10 2014.
Hampton T. & Blakeley K. "Anti-Anxiety Drugs Might Rebalance Autistic
Brain." *News Beat UW Health Sciences.* Mar. 2014. Web 10 June 2014.
Lader, M. H., M. Ron, and H. Petursson. "Computed Axial Brain
Tomography in Long-Term Benzodiazepine Users." *Psychological
Medicine* 14, (1984): 203-06.
Lakhani, Nina. "Drugs Linked to Brain Damage 30 Years Ago. *The
Independent.* 2010. Web. 10 June 2014.
Lane, Christopher. "Brain Damage from Benzodiazepines: The Troubling
Facts, Risks, and History of Minor Tranquilizers." *Psychology Today*
2010. Web. 10 June 2014.
Maron, D. F. "Antianxiety Drugs Successfully Treat Autism." *Scientific
American.* Mar. 2014. Web. 10 June 2014.

Chapter 13
Angell M, The Truth About the Drug Companies, *The New York Review of
Books*, July 15, 2004
Krystal, John H. "Dr. Marcia Angell and the Illusions of Anti-Psychiatry."
Psychiatric Times. Aug. 2012. Web. 10 June 2014.
Whitaker, Robert. *"Anatomy of an Epidemic: Magic Bullets, Psychiatric
Drugs, and the Astonishing Rise of Mental Illness in America."* New
York: Crown, 2010.

Chapter 14
Brody, Howard. *"Hooked: Ethics, the Medical Profession and the
Pharmaceutical Industry."* Lanham, Maryland: Rowan & Littlefield
Publishers, 2007.
Brody, Howard. "Pradaxa: More Evidence of Drug Firms Manipulating
Science." *Hooked: Ethics, Medicine, and Pharma.* Blogger 23 Feb.
2014. Web 11 June 2014.

Whitaker, Robert. "SAMHSA, Alternatives, and a Psychiatrist's Despair Over the State of American Science." *Psychology Today.* 10 Oct. 2010. Web June 11 2014.

Chapter 15

Ashton, C. H. "Benzodiazepines: How They Work and How to Withdraw." *The Ashton Manual,* 2002.

Maine Benzodiazepine Study Group. University of Maine Center on Aging, Oct. 2011. Web. 05 June 2014.

Lane, Christopher. "Brain Damage from Benzodiazepines: The Troubling Facts, Risks, and History of Minor Tranquilizers." *Psychology Today* 2010. Web. 10 June 2014.

Chapter 19

Berensen, A., Harris, G., Meier, B., and Pollack, A. "Despite Warnings, Drug Giant Took Long Path to Vioxx Recall." *The New York Times.* November 2004. Web. 20 July 2014.

Prakash, S., Valentine, Vikki. "Timeline: The Rise and Fall of Vioxx." *NPR.* 10 Nov. 2007. Web 22 July 2014.

"The War Against America; The National Defense." Editorial. *The New York Times.* 12 September 2001. Web. 22 July 2014.

Substance Abuse and Mental Health Services Administration. (2011). "Evaluation of the Protection and Advocacy for Individuals With Mental Illness (PAIMI) Program, Phase III. Final Report." *HHS Pub. No. PEP12-EVALPAIMI.* Rockville, MD: Center for Mental Health Services, Substance Abuse and Mental Health Service Administration.

Chapter 21

Ashton, C. H. "Benzodiazepines: How They Work and How to Withdraw." *The Ashton Manual,* 2002.

Balt, Steve. "Two New Ways to Get Sued." *The Carlat Psychiatry Blog.* Jan. 2012. Web 12 June 2014.

Lane, Christopher. "Brain Damage from Benzodiazepines: The Troubling Facts, Risks, and History of Minor Tranquilizers." *Psychology Today* 2010. Web. 10 June 2014.

Chapter 23

Diamond, Jared. *"Collapse: How Societies Choose to Fail or Succeed."* New York, NY: Viking Penguin, 2005.

Harris, Gardiner. "Drug Makers Are Advocacy Group's Biggest Donors." *The New York Times.* Oct. 2009. Web 16 June 2014.

Kerth, Rob., Vinyard, Shelley. "Wasting Our Waterways 2012: Toxic Industrial Pollution and the Unfulfilled Promise of the Clean Water Act." *Environment America Research & Policy Center*, 2012. Web 25 June 2014.

Lang, Susan S. "Water, Air and Soil Pollution Causes 40 Percent of Deaths Worldwide, Cornell Research Survey Finds." Cornell Chronicle. Aug. 2007. Web. 23 June 2014.

Resolution
Kraus, Mark L. "The Dangers of Legalizing Medical Marijuana: A Physician's Perspective." *Ct Chapter American Society of Addiction Medicine*. 26 Feb. 2007. Web 07 July 2014.

Li, Guohua. "Marijuana Use May Double the Risk of Accidents for Drivers." *Columbia University Mailman School of Public Health*. 6 Oct 2011. Web. 07 July 2014.

Mann, Charles C. "State of the Species: Does Success Spell Doom for Homo Sapiens?" *Orion Magazine*. Nov/Dec 2012. Web 11 June 2014.

Snowbeck, Christopher. "Legalize Medical Marijuana? Many Doctors Hesitant." *Twin Cities Dot Com Pioneer Press.* 10 Mar. 2014. Web 07 July 2014.

ACKNOWLEDGMENTS

Acknowledgments are that part of a book I've often read hoping someday I might get to make something like that up. While authors expressed gratitude for the generous souls without whom their books would not have been published, I wracked my brain wondering who those people would be for me. Luckily, I got to find out.

Melissa McNeill is a friend who believed it was important for me to tell my story and gave generous encouragement while I finished writing it. She read through my first draft and provided invaluable feedback from a mental health practitioner's perspective.

Shawn Svoboda-Barber was another encourager who took the time to read through the second draft and give additional feedback.

Angela Pancella gave generously of her time to provide important feedback and help with the final copy editing.

Karen Novak enthusiastically picked up and read the manuscript, making wise suggestions that helped me rewrite the story into a more complete and personal one. She offered lavish encouragement, sound advice, and useful information, as well as helped prepare the final draft.

Suzanne Mills, who created the Alice in Wonderland illustration, also assisted with aspects of the book's cover design and was an absolute joy to work with.

My friend and fellow author, Kenny Oster, has been a constant source of encouragement in all of the years it has taken me to write this book. He believed the story was important and needed to be told, and continued to remind me even when I had stopped writing it. He listened tirelessly, read multiple drafts at various stages, and gave feedback, as well as assisted with the crucial task of copy editing.

Lastly, I am indebted to the two most patient and empathetic kids any parent could ask for, the kids who loved me while we lived the story, and who became the adults that would cheer me on as I put those experiences into a book.

ACKNOWLEDGMENTS
Part Two

Acknowledgments are that part of a book I've often read hoping someday I might get to make something like that up. While authors expressed gratitude for the generous souls without whom their books would not have been published, I wracked my brain wondering how on earth I would even finish mine. My brain was continually taxed by severe, chronic insomnia, and writing, especially about pharmaceutical corruption and all that had happened to me, was torture. I held onto the manuscript anyway, not knowing how it would ever get done. Luckily, I got to find out.

I began using cannabis medicinally in the early part of 2014. This was after my practitioners had given me the boot and I was desperate to find relief from the ever-present insomnia. Taking an illegal drug was a last resort. Obtaining, possessing and using marijuana was not comfortable behavior for me, but I wanted to continue supporting myself and to be there for the people I care about. By this point, whatever I thought the consequences might be, I couldn't afford to worry about them.

After I became adjusted to using cannabis, I was able to sleep a bit more and to function somewhat more comfortably. It still holds true that it did not solve all of my problems, and I still can't say this was the answer I had been looking for. But what I can say is that by using marijuana medicinally, the door was opened for me to begin writing again, and that was how I was finally able to finish writing my story. Acknowledgments for what made this book possible would be nowhere near complete without making mention of that fact.

Made in the USA
Columbia, SC
25 June 2019